Thomas Telford: Engineer

Tho! Telford

Thomas Telford: Engineer

Proceedings of a seminar held at the Coalport China Works Museum, Ironbridge, April 1979, under the auspices of the Ironbridge Gorge Museum Trust and Telford Development Corporation

Edited by Alastair Penfold, BA, MPhil

Foreword by Dr Neil Cossons, MA, FSA, FMA

Thomas Telford Ltd: London: 1980

First published in 1980 by Thomas Telford Ltd,
PO Box 101, 23–34 Old Street, London EC1P 1JH

Production Editor: M. Monro

© Ironbridge Gorge Museum Trust, 1980

ISBN 0 7277 0084 7

Photoset printed and bound in Great Britain by
Redwood Burn Limited, Trowbridge & Esher

Contents

Foreword

NEIL COSSONS

The Thomas Telford seminar, held at the Coalport China Works Museum, in April 1979, marked the culmination of a project by staff of the Ironbridge Gorge Museum Trust and Telford Development Coporation to stimulate interest and research into the life and works of Thomas Telford.

The aim of the seminar was to provide an up-to-date summary of current research by leading experts on Telford with special emphasis on his government projects and early years in Shropshire. An attempt was made to maintain a balance between technical and historical papers and the transactions should appeal to historians and civil engineers alike.

The son of an Eskdale shepherd, Telford was born in August 1757 at Glendinning, in the Parish of Westerkirk near Langholm, Dumfriesshire. His father died the same year. Brought up in great hardship by his widowed mother, Telford attended the local parish school where he obtained a basic education before becoming apprenticed to a stone-mason in 1770. His subsequent training as a mason provided him with the practical knowledge which was so essential in his later career. He worked with Andrew Thompson, a Langholm stonemason, on Langholm 'New Town', part of an improvement scheme financed by the Duke of Buccleugh, and on Langholm Bridge, where his mason's work can still be seen on the western abutment. He developed an early passion for reading and writing poetry which remained until his death in 1834.

Telford left Eskdale for the first time in 1780, gaining further practical experience as a mason in Edinburgh. Determined to improve his position, he made a careful study of architectural styles and methods, hoping one day to become an architect. He left for London in 1782, gaining employment as a mason on Somerset

House before his first managerial appointment as Building Superintendent for the new Commissioner's House at Portsmouth Naval Dockyard in 1784.

During this period Telford met William Pulteney, MP for Shrewsbury, whose friendship and patronage was to play a vital role in furthering his career. Pulteney commissioned Telford to design and supervise the restoration of Shrewsbury Castle, and it was through his influence that Telford obtained the post of Surveyor of Public Works for the county of Salop in 1787 – a post he was to retain for life. It was while working as surveyor that Telford began to build up the team of assistants and contractors which was to serve him so well in later years. Still regarded primarily as an architect rather than as a civil engineer, Telford was responsible for the design and construction of public buildings and bridges in Shropshire, including Montford and Buildwas bridges. He employed Matthew Davidson, his former colleague from Langholm, as site engineer at Montford, whilst John Simpson undertook the masonry work. In both instances it was to mark the beginning of a long association with Telford which was only severed after Simpson's death in 1815 and Davidson's in 1819.

Telford's appointment as General Agent to the Ellesmere Canal Company in 1795 marked the beginning of his long association with canals. Working under William Jessop, Telford's duties were described in some detail by the Board in the Autumn of 1793:

> Mr Thomas Telford of Shrewsbury, Architect . . . [is] appointed the General Agent, Surveyor, Engineer, architect and overlooker of the canal and clerk to this Committee and the sub-committees. [He is] . . . to make reports, to superintend the cutting, forming and making the canal and taking up and seeing to the due observance of the levels thereof, to make the drawings and to submit such drawings to the Committee. . . . to give instruction for contracts to attend by himself . . . to pay the contractors' workmen and other persons employed in the execution of the said works and keep the accounts of the concern regularly . . . His engagement to extend to all architecture and engineering business, to the drawing, forming and directing the making of bridges, aqueducts, locks, building reservoirs, wharfs and other works in and about completing the said canal.

He was to be paid £500 year.

There were several other engineers on the project and his position at first must have been rather ambiguous. However, his dominant personality soon made him second only to Jessop. He was responsible for the design of the major aqueducts at Chirk and Pontcysyllte, using Davidson as resident engineer and Simpson (with Wilson and Cargill) as masonry contractor. William Hazledine was given the contract for the ironwork, whilst another future Caledonian Canal contractor, William Davies, undertook the massive earthen embankment leading up to the aqueduct.

The Pulteney connection had brought Telford, at a very early date, in contact with the British Fisheries Society. This in turn led to his involvement in the Treasury's surveys of the highlands in 1801 and 1802 and in the setting up of the two boards of commissioners for the Caledonian Canal and highland roads and bridges in 1803.

Full scale construction work on both these projects ceased by the early 1820s, by which time Telford had become the country's most eminent civil engineer, having accepted the Presidency of the newly formed Institution of Civil Engineers in 1820. He was involved in numerous projects which ran concurrently with the highland works, the most prominent being the Götha Canal in Sweden and the improvement of the London to Holyhead Road which commenced in 1815. This was his second government-financed scheme and included the bridging of the Menai Straits by the one of the world's first major suspension bridge. He again used many of his well tried assistants and contractors and the whole project can, with justification, be regarded as his greatest triumph, both in terms of technical brilliance and organization. The road between Shrewsbury and Holyhead, which Telford rebuilt completely, was described at the time of its completion in the 1830s as 'a model of the most perfect road making that has ever been attempted in any country'. His most famous work, the Menai Bridge, was completed in 1826, the links for its suspension chains being manufactured by William Hazledine whilst Wilson undertook the masonry contract.

Telford was employed throughout the 1820s and early 30s on numerous canal improvement schemes, including a realignment of the Birmingham Canal which included the excavation of the summit level at Smethwick and the construction of a second tunnel through Harecastle Hill. Both projects show the huge technical advances made in the practice and organization of civil engineering in the half century since the death of Brindley, Harecastle Tunnel alone being completed in a fraction of the time taken by the builders of the first tunnel. His last canal, the Birmingham and Liverpool Junction, which shortened the canal route between Birmingham and the Mersey by nearly 20 miles, was not completed until a year after his death, due mainly to technical problems at Shelmore embankment.

Throughout the 1820s Telford acted as Engineer to the Exchequer Bill Loan Commission Board, a body set up to ease the unemployment problem through the granting of financial aid to civil engineering schemes. Acting in this capacity Telford became involved with virtually all the major civil engineering projects of the period, including the Liverpool and Manchester Railway and the Gloucester and Berkeley Canal.

Illness and old age caused Telford to decline new commissions after 1828, and he concentrated on finishing those in hand and compiling his autobiography, which remained unpublished at the time of his death in September 1834. He was buried in Westminster Abbey.

A life so full of distinction and variety would be difficult to encompass in the course of a short seminar and has already been covered both by Telford himself and his subsequent biographers. While dealing with some of the major projects of his career, the papers therefore concentrate on casting new light not only on Telford's engineering genius, but also on his contribution to the social and historical development of Britain during the 19th century which he did so much to nurture.

~ 1 ~

Thomas Telford in Shrewsbury

The metamorphosis of an architect into a civil engineer

J. B. LAWSON

When Thomas Telford came to Shrewsbury in late 1786 or early 1787 he was almost 30 and had still to make his reputation and establish himself. Trained as a mason in Eskdale, he had migrated to London, earned the approbation of Robert Adam and Sir William Chambers, but failed in his ambition to set up in business as a contractor. Employed by Samuel Wyatt to superintend building works at Portsmouth dockyard, he found plenty of time for study. Meanwhile he had in 1783–84 already worked for his future patron and countryman, William Pulteney at Sudborough Rectory, Northants, where one of his closest future acquaintances, Archibald Alison, was rector. Work for Sir James Johnstone of Westerhall, Pulteney's elder brother, followed.

Telford had acquired a varied experience, worked under able men, had boundless energy and intellectual curiosity, but there was no guarantee that William Pulteney's invitation to restore Shrewsbury Castle would lead to a brilliant career as an architect, let alone as a civil engineer. The purpose of this paper is to re-examine his early Shrewsbury years, to review the work he did, see what friends he made and the manner in which his professional skill, energy and competence quickly earned him a reputation which opened the way to a career in civil engineering which he correctly perceived in 1793 had far greater rewards to offer than the architectural odd-jobbery which a provincial town like Shrewsbury and its hinterland could offer.

His reputation was established by architectural practice both public and private, and his achievement as a person between 1786 and 1793 is best summarized from the diary of Catherine Plymley, the sister of one of his closest supporters and friends, Archdeacon Joseph Plymley. Writing in November 1793, a few days after Telford's appointment as General Agent to the Ellesmere Canal, she records an evening spent in the company of Archibald Alison and Telford:

> 'I have not often spent so pleasant an evening . . . Mr. Telford is a man I highly respect. Born of poor parents . . . brought up a common work-ing mason, he has by uncommon genius and unwearied industry raised himself to be an excellent Architect and a most intelligent and enlight-ened man. His knowledge is general, his conversation very animated, his look full of intelligence and vivacity. He is eminently chearful and the broad scotch accent that he retains rather becomes him. He has been settled in Shrewsbury for some few years . . . and has been engaged in many public and private buildings, he is the architect for the new church at Madeley and has just received a very advantageous appoint-ment . . . But praise of a higher kind belongs to him, what he procures by his merit and industry he bestows most benevolently and liberally: frugal in his own expenses, he can do more for others, and what he does he does chearfully.'[1]

The last sentence bears out much of what he wrote to Andrew Little, and for his philanthropy John Rickman and his correspon-dents provide evidence, even if the details are obscure.[2]

Early years

Telford arrived in Shrewsbury the protégé of William Pulte-ney, one of the MPs for the town, resided in his house – Shrews-bury Castle – and was closely identified with a political faction in strong opposition to Lord Clive. Pulteney was austere, serious, socially concerned, fabulously rich, and had wide estates. Shrews-bury was still very much a mediaeval town, with squalid streets which an Improvement Act of 1756 had done little to improve, but there was a spirit of change abroad, especially amongst the county magistrates. The architectural fraternity, which served a wide hin-terland, was a little pedestrian and possibly corrupt. There had been, and still was, a strong tradition of builder architects, where the dividing line between architect and contractor was blurred and where architect contractors shared their commissions with their competitors in other trades. Such were the Haycocks, Scoltocks, Carlines and Joseph Bromfield; carpenters, bricklayers, masons, and a plasterer. Particularly where public works were concerned, there was no man of sufficient integrity and independence to oversee contracts, and in this situation the arrival of a man like Telford was fortunate. Unconnected with the tradesmen of the town, with a reputation to make and frugal in his own expenditure, he had no axe to grind, and the fact that he had no capital did not matter.

His immediate concern on arrival was the remodelling of the Castle as an occasional residence for his patron. This was already under way by January 1787, and was accomplished in Gothic style and, according to Catherine Plymley 'in true taste'. Of his work there only survives a delightful room in one of the towers, with an exquisite ogee arched Gothic fireplace, and Laura's Tower, a picturesque Gothic summerhouse with a groined plaster vault. Already he was employed on public works under the Shirehall Act, surveying the widening of High Street, then notoriously narrow. This was a ticklish business, involving the demolition and rebuilding of a large number of houses.[3] In the private sector he was engaged by John Edwards of Great Ness to redevelop the site of the Raven Inn in Castle Street as a square. Plans for this ingenious enterprise survive and include a sketch of a complete scheme of decoration for a gracious room overlooking the Severn.[4] The eating rooms in two of the houses include one round and one apsidal room, perhaps showing the influence of Samuel Wyatt.[5]

His appointment as clerk of works at the new gaol in late July 1787 was a great step forward. Employed at a salary of £60 a year, he came under the scrutiny of a small influential and progressive minded committee of county magistrates. With a 'character' provided by Robert Adam, he was employed on terms which stipulated that he should have no part in the contracts.[6] The gaol had been designed by John Hiram Haycock, who had recently designed and completed the new Shirehall, but the magistrates had had some contact with William Blackburn, the architectural interpreter of the ideas of John Howard, the prison reformer, and in February 1788 Howard came to inspect the plans in person. He disliked the size of the interior courts and the chapel, and in consequence Telford made a 'thorough reformation' and 'new modelling' of Haycock's design.[7] As no original plans have survived, his impact cannot be assessed, but the octagonal chapel is surely his and the rocky rusticated entrance towers facing the Castle walls seem totally unlike any work by Haycock. Telford's opinion of Haycock may not have been high, as in later life he describes him merely as a 'builder of Shrewsbury.'[8]

Howard also inspected the Salop Infirmary,[9] founded in 1745, where Telford had just been appointed architect after the rejection of a design by Samuel Scoltock, which had previously been approved.[10] He added two wings to the early 18th century house, which were built by the Haycocks. By their 'incongruity of style' these were said to have 'defaced the elevation' of the existing building, but despite the clash of styles, the facilities were 'greatly improved'.[11] In conjunction with the works at the Gaol he was responsible for road widening on Castle Gates, the northern entry to the town, where he also made changes in the gardens of Shrewsbury School, probably occasioned by the removal of one of the town gates.[12]

St Chad's and other churches

The first two years in Shrewsbury had been highly productive and had included an unidentified country house. Of his earliest commissions one was to have spectacular consequences.[13] In May 1788 he was sent by William Pulteney to survey St Chad's Church, Shrewsbury, where the parishioners were quarrelling over a leaking roof, although later accounts suggest that structural weakness was already suspected. Telford reported that:

> 'In the course of my examining the state of the roof I discovered that there were large fractures in the walls, on tracing which I found that the whole was in a most shattered condition, tho' till now scarcely noticed.'

The cause of the trouble was the fractured NW pier of the tower which had fissured and sunk following unwise gravedigging. Worse still, the nave and roof timbers were badly decayed, and so were the walls, and Telford feared that further lateral spread would be fatal to the structure. His warnings fell on unreceptive ears.

> 'These fractures were said to be there from time immemorial – and it was said by even sensible people that Professional men always wish'd to carve out employment for themselves and that the whole might be done at a small expense which they proceeded to do.'

The vestry employed a mason to hack away the fractured parts of

Fig. 1. The fall of Old St Chad's (Watercolour by Rev. Edward Williams, 1787)

the pier without supporting the massive weight of the tower and bells, and in the early morning of 9 July the tower fell neatly through the roof of the nave:

> 'The very parts I had pointed out gave way and down tumbled the mighty mass forming a very magnificent ruin' (Fig. 1).

As he had left the fateful vestry meeting, nettled by his reception, he had told them 'that if they wished to discuss anything besides the alarming state of the church they had better adjourn to some other place where there was no danger of its falling on their heads'. The outcome proved the integrity and honesty of the man and reflected poorly on the standing and competence of contemporary Shrewsbury architects and builders.

Following the fall of St Chad's an unholy alliance of builders and architects advised the demolition of St Alkmund's, allegedly because it was structurally unsound and uneconomic to repair. Rebuilt by Messrs Carline and Tilley between 1793 and 1795 employing the Haycocks and Joseph Bromfield as sub-contractors, the building had severe structural problems within 10 years from lateral spread of the roof, which required expensive remedial works.[14]

In view of the fate of St Alkmund's and St Chad's, the church of St. Mary was lucky to have Telford as its restorer. The principles on which he acted firmly respected the past. His prime concern was the safety of the fabric, followed by the prevention of further decay. Features should only be rebuilt where they would be un-economic to repair and only when funds permitted should cos-metic work be undertaken.[15] He restored the chancel for the impropriators of the tithes in 1787–88.[16] By September 1788 he had made a new pulpit in the Gothic style which he believed 'carried off more applause than the sermon' at the annual anniversary service of the Salop Infirmary[17].

During the 1790s new pews, organ loft and Mayor's seat were made at prices approved by him, but by September 1798 the fabric was causing alarm. Acting probably on the advice of the anti-quarian vicar, John Brickdale Blakeway, the vestry consulted the Lichfield ecclesiastical architect, Joseph Potter. When nothing had come of this by March 1799, Telford, John Simpson and Richard Lee, a carpenter, devised a carefully phased programme of restora-tion depending on categories of urgency or desirability.[18] Severe defects were found in nave and side aisle roofs, tower, spire and bell-frame. The fine 15th century roof was in danger of collapse and was bolted through to a new roof covered with Westmoreland slate, instead of lead, to lessen the thrust. The exterior walls were to be cut back to sound stone and pointed and a leaning arcade was to be buttressed. The level of the churchyard against the walls was to be lowered and proper drains laid down to carry away rainwater. Amongst the least essential works was the decoration of the tran-sept roofs either by painting them as in the chapel and library of Shrewsbury School, or by plastering with groined Gothic stucco. As a good student of Gothic architecture, he finally advised that the nave roof and tower should have pinnacles restored to them.[19] Most of the work had been completed by 1801.[20]

Whilst the initial work at St Mary's was in progress, Telford had obtained a brief for £1200 at the autumn Quarter Sessions in 1789 for the restoration of All Saints' Baschurch.[21] There the north aisle walls were demolished and the chancel largely rebuilt at the expense of the impropriators of the tithes, the total cost amounting

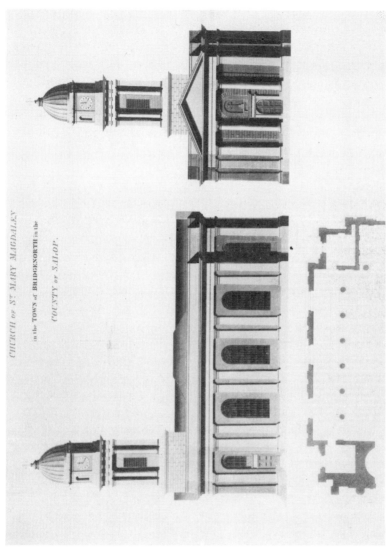

Fig. 2. St Mary Magdalen Bridgnorth (Telford Atlas)

to a little under £1200 by May 1791.[22] This was followed by work
at Cleobury Mortimer in 1793 where he had recently surveyed a
bridge. The parish consulted him as to the desirability of building a
new church in place of the old which was endangered by lateral
spread. He solved the problem by inserting strong wooden tie
beams across the nave, concealed by a plaster ceiling.[23] The result
was hardly beautiful, but it was structurally effective.

Restorations went hand-in-hand with new churches. The first of
which was St Mary Magdalene, Bridgnorth, (Fig. 2) where an Act
had been obtained early in 1792. Well aware of the townscape possibilities of the new church, he orientated it accordingly. 'The
entrance end of the New church is to front and nearly fill the end of
the principal street and one side is to show itself to the lower Town
and adjacent country – The Tower and Cupola will be seen in all
directions.'[24] He was diffident about the design: 'Its only merit is
simplicity and uniformity . . . A regularly Ionic interior, a Tuscan
elevation, and a Doric Tower.'[25] Sir Nikolaus Pevsner calls it a
'remarkable design, of great gravity inside and out, and apparently
done in full awareness of recent developments in France.'[26] When
designing it in March 1792 Telford borrowed Montfaucon's *Antiquities*, vol. II and Stuart and Revett's *Antiquities of Athens*, vol. I
from Shrewsbury School Library.[27] This almost square church was
carefully planned, with good acoustics, to bring the congregation
as close to the pulpit as possible and with the minimum of distrac-
tions. He eschewed 'an offensive number of trifling parts'[28] inside
by using arcades of unfluted Ionic columns to support the roof, and
by lighting the church with three large, arched windows on each
side. There was a blank east wall occupied by the altar-piece, thus
avoiding the dazzling glare which proved so troublesome at St
Chad's, Shrewsbury.

The exterior is equally severe: describing the tower to a corre-
spondent, (probably Thomas Haslewood, the Bridgnorth solicitor
who was examined on the Bill by the House of Commons
committee[29]) he says: 'instead of several cham [sic] ranges of different and expensive orders of Columns above one another, there is
here only a basement of the Tower, one height of columns round
the space allotted for the Bells, and an apartment for the Clock and a
Dome . . .'.[30] – a severely practical design, which might have been
a muted criticism of George Steuart's St Chad's, Shrewsbury,

which Telford had watched in building and which contemporary critics, with justice, accused of being a diversity of disjointed parts, lacking homogeneity.

Further developments

Whilst the church was still being built in March 1793, and just before he set out on his architectural study tour to Bath, London and Oxford, Telford undertook to design the new church at Madeley in the heart of industrial East Shropshire. When the design was approved in October 1793 he described it as a 'very peculiar construction' (Fig. 3). Octagonal outside, but oblong within, it had a square west tower. Tuscan and Adamish columns supported the galleries and roof inside and the east wall had a Venetian window which was to be fitted with glass by Francis Eginton of Birmingham.[31]

Fig. 3. St Michael's Madeley

At this stage he seems to have had no premonition that his architectural career was drawing to a close. His architectural study tour was carried through with characteristic thoroughness, with careful appraisals of contemporary buildings in Bath, Oxford and London, especially the extensive Gothic works of James Wyatt in Oxford, but not neglecting the architects of the past, of whom he singled out Dean Aldrich of Christchurch, Oxford, for particular praise. In Oxford he enthused over the Guise Old Master collection at Christchurch and the Arundel marbles, as well as collections in London, where he studied and noted a large number of architectural books in the British Museum and the library of the Society of Antiquaries. These included works by or of Vitruvius, Palladio and Inigo Jones and Sir William Chambers on Chinese architecture.[32] As Catherine Plymley was to remark later in the year a man of 'true taste'.

However, at the end of 1793 his appointment to the Ellesmere canal led him 'positively to decline meddling with House Building in any shape', except for three favoured clients: Archdeacon Plymley, Joseph Loxdale (town clerk of Shrewsbury and clerk of the peace, 1802–1833) and Isaac Hawkins Browne of Badger Hall (MP for Bridgnorth 1784–1812).[33] Quite what he did for Plymley is uncertain; for Loxdale he almost certainly built Kingsland House on Kingsland, Shrewsbury, which had an octagonal walled garden,[34] and for Browne one can only speculate. He was a coal proprietor in Madeley, a magistrate, the mouthpiece of the Birmingham manufacturers in Parliament and had piloted the Act for the new church at Bridgnorth through the House of Commons. There are many good reasons why Telford should have known him well. Although he may have done work at Badger, which had been built by James Wyatt between 1779 and 1783, he almost certainly planned the octagonal church of St Leonards, Malins Lee, which Browne built in 1805 and which is similar in design to Madeley.[35]

Enough has been said of his architectural practice to indicate its content. It was interspersed with forays into Romano-British antiquity on the Pulteney estate at Wroxeter in 1788 and at Lea near Pontesbury in 1793. He may have had the oversight of dilapidations and repairs on William Pulteney's estate in Shropshire and certainly made experiments in land drainage for him.[36] He probably surveyed the North Yorkshire estate of the Marquis of Stafford at Snittenham in early 1790 under the eye of John Bishton but there seems to be no evidence that he had competed with Bishton for the General Agency of Stafford's estate in 1788.[37]

However, of more importance for the future was his appointment as county surveyor of bridges. Although plans of a 'public bridge' were referred to him as early as January 1787 the first bridge he surveyed was at Meole over the Rea brook, near Shrewsbury in 1788 where he decided against a bridge by Messrs Carline and Tilley in favour of a scheme by John Nelson, a former craftsman of T. F. Pritchard.[38] Thereafter he was 'regularly employed as the surveyor of an extensive county'.[39] There was no formal appointment and no annual salary. He was paid either a percentage of the contract or 'by a bill for plans, estimates, time, trouble, horsehire and Expenses'.[40]

As surveyor he was fortunate in being appointed at a time when the active magistrates of the Quarter Sessions were increasingly willing to extend the range of their activities. His early relations with the Sessions were complicated by 'contention,' in which he says he was 'always the prominent feature' and the problem may have been his political identification with his patron William Pulteney in opposition to Lord Clive.[41] Writing of the magistrates in January 1788 he compliments them as

'. . . having once interested themselves and publicly declared their opinion, it becomes their own act, and redounds to their honour, to render their Surveyor respectable, and on my part it requires a continual something to keep the spirit awake'.[42]

He persuaded them to allow him to use convict labour at Wroxeter, on the building of the Gaol and later at Montford Bridge.[43] He stirred them into activity over county bridges in April 1789, when legal opinion was consulted as to the magistrates' powers, and in October he had a hard fight during the Sessions over the rebuilding of Chirk and Montford bridges:[44] 'I was obliged to speak a good deal, and even bully a little – some of these fellows are ignorant and obstinate, tho' I must say that upon the whole there is a very respectable Bench of Justices, and with the sensible part I believe I am on good terms.'[45]

Montford Bridge, built 1790–92 set a pattern which was to be repeated many times in the future. Built of red, Nesscliffe stone, of

three elliptical arches on piers built in coffer dams, it was the first
bridge supervised by his old friend Matthew Davidson, who was
brought down from Langholm specially to supervise Messrs Carline and Tilley.[46] Major works followed at Buildwas in 1791 and at
Chirk in 1793 where the detailed specifications underline Telford's
mastery of masonry detail.[47] The work was carried out by John
Simpson and supervised by Davidson. The same year he and Simpson concurred in advising that the position and alignment of the
new Welsh Bridge at Shrewsbury should not be 'placed upon a gra-
velly ford, and in an improper direction' but were ignored. Forty
years later Telford had to remind the corporation of their folly
when recommending essential remedial works.[48]

The move to civil engineering
The years 1793 and 1795 saw the emergence of Telford as a civil
engineer. He was appointed General Agent to the Ellesmere Canal
in late October 1793 and Engineer to the Shrewsbury Canal in
February 1795 following the death of Josiah Clowes. It may be
wondered why he was chosen for such a bold enterprise as the
Ellesmere Canal. William Jessop had done the spade work and
remained an important consultant, but could not undertake the
general supervision of the works.[49] Telford perhaps explains it best
himself

> ' . . . the committee of management composed chiefly of county magi-
> strates, having at the Quarter Sessions and their public meeting,
> observed that the county works were conducted to their satisfaction,
> were pleased to propose my undertaking the conduct of this extensive
> and complicated work and feeling in myself a stronger disposition for
> executing works of importance and magnitude than for the details of
> house architecture I did not hesitate to accept their offer.'[50]

He travelled to the general meeting in the carriage of 'the great John
Wilkinson, king of the Iron Masters' and considered himself 'fortunate in being on good terms with most of the leading men of property and abilities'.[51]

These new responsibilities made an end of his architectural
career, except for favoured clients, and it would seem with few
regrets. He reserved the right to continue practising, but only
where day-to-day supervision was not required:

'I shall retain all I wish for of that, which are the Public Building and Houses of importance. The other parts of our business are better to be without; they give a great deal of unpleasant labour for very little profit, in short they are like the calls of a Country Surgeon. These I shall give up without reluctance, except what relates to Mr Pulteney and Lady Bath.'[52]

As he admitted to Archdeacon Corbet (Plymley) in 1805 'the profession of a Civil Engineer has opened a much wider field, and to me a much more agreeable pursuit'.[53]

It was certainly an arduous life, for in 1795 in addition to the canal works, he was faced with the consequences of the February floods, which had caused widespread damage to bridges on the Severn and its tributaries. In March he claimed that he was 'at it night and day' which is not surprising, for by 18 March he had completed the plans for the cast iron aqueduct at Longdon-on-Tern, designed Bewdley Bridge and made plans for an abortive new bridge over the Severn at Bridgnorth.[54] The new iron bridge for Buildwas had been designed by 14 April, when at the Quarter Sessions he was further ordered to survey bridges at Ashford (over the Teme), Cound, Shawbury, Ternhill, Strefford and Longdon. Later he surveyed bridges at Great Bolas, Pontesford and Ryton.[55] Of these the only major bridge was at Ashford where the single masonry arch of 80 ft, with hollowed spandrels, was completed in 1797.[56] At Cound a cast-iron bridge was erected, but not to Telford's design and he had to replace it in 1818.[57] Outside the county at Bewdley the bridge trustees considered a number of schemes but eventually in the very dry summer and autumn of 1798 the bridge was raised 'by enchantment in one season, which is no contemptible work, for John Simpson and your humble servant.' Simpson had been recommended as contractor by Joseph Loxdale, town clerk of Shrewsbury and one of Telford's close associates. The bridge with its classical balustrades, segmental arches and green and pink stone is arguably one of the most elegant in England.[58]

The major works of 1795, and by far the most exciting, were those in iron: Buildwas Bridge (Fig. 4), Longdon Aqueduct and the spade work for the spectacular Pontcysyllte Aqueduct, whose design is considered in detail by Hadfield and Skempton.[59] Buildwas Bridge, for which his plans and a model made by the

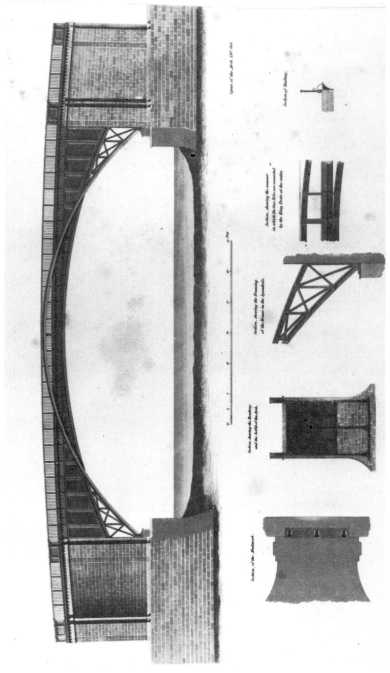

Fig. 4. Buildwas Bridge (Telford Atlas)

Coalbrookdale Company were laid before the Quarter Sessions in April 1795, were referred to William Reynolds and John Wilkinson for their opinions. The company apparently disapproved of the low rise design, but it was preferred.[60] The Schaffhausen principle which Telford used for the arch appears to have been quite well known amongst English engineers at the time, and was applied for good reasons.[61] In 1800 he said that he used it because 'the roadway could not with propriety be raised to a great height' and had to be kept as level as possible with the banks.[62] Moreover the uncommonly high flood had led him to consider a design 'which would avoid piers and allow for rapid changes in river level' and, more cogently, because of the instability of the banks, he used 'a very flat arch (the segment of a very large circle, calculated to resist the abutments if disposed to slide inwards, as at Coalbrookdale)'. The back of each abutment was 'wedge shape, so as to throw off laterally much of the pressure of the earth'.[63]

Apart from these design considerations, tests were made on iron bars at Ketley in March 1795 and on ribs at Coalbrookdale in April. The latter were almost certainly concerned with Buildwas Bridge and the former with the vertical columns of the Longdon Aqueduct.[64] According to Telford the use of cast iron for the aqueduct was the suggestion of Thomas Eyton, the Shrewsbury banker, chairman of the canal committee and also banker to the Ellesmere canal.[65] Although the design was approved on 14 March, extensive experiments were made by William Reynolds at Ketley and the result was very much a collaboration. It is in no sense an arched structure but rather an iron beam made up of cast-iron sections and supported by pillars and struts.[66] The design of Pontycysllte was totally different and there can be no doubt that William Jessup had a hand in it, but in view of the confidence which the local community had in Telford and the experience which he had already gained with iron, the decision of the canal company on 8 July, 1795, to build a cast iron aqueduct is not surprising.

When one considers the technical sophistication of Buildwas and Longdon it is a little surprising to find Telford responsible for a wooden bridge built across the Severn at Cressage in 1799–1801 to replace a ferry (Fig. 5). Cast iron was amongst the materials mentioned in the Act authorizing the bridge, but probably on grounds of economy it was built of timber, costing just under £4000 in con-

Fig. 5. Cressage Bridge, c. 1900

trast to over £6400 for Buildwas. It had five spans carried on four wooden piers and stone abutments built by John Simpson. Telford was himself among the shareholders, and at the time had an interest in the Lower Longwood colliery mentioned in the Act on the north side of the river. This was probably connected with a lime-kiln on Wenlock Edge in which both he and Simpson were concerned. The link road from the bridge to the so-called Leighton turnpike was probably the first extensive stretch of road engineered by Telford.[67]

Friends and colleagues

The period between 1786 and 1793 saw his brief career as an architect in Shrewsbury, the period from 1793 marked him out as an innovating civil engineer capable of daring projects. By 1793 he had the confidence of the Quarter Sessions and landed gentry as well as men of 'abilities', and had already made many of the friends amongst practical men and scientists which were to abide throughout his life. William Hazledine, the millwright and iron founder, had supplied a pump to the Gaol, they were both members of the Salopian Lodge and on intimate terms. He was an ingenious inventor and Telford referred to him in early 1796 as 'the Arch conjuror himself, Merlin Hazledine'.[68] It is probable that Telford knew the details of the first iron frame building, the flax mill at Ditherington in Shrewsbury, which was designed by Charles Bage and cast by Hazledine in 1796–97. Bage's experiments on the strength of iron bars are recorded in Telford's memorandum book and it seems likely that Bage borrowed the results of the Ketley experiment by Reynolds for the Longdon Aqueduct in 1795.[69] Bage had worked with Telford on survey work at the Gaol in 1788 and at Madeley.[70]

John Simpson, his inseparable companion from 1793 on innumerable contracts until his death in 1815, was an able mason from Stenhouse, Midlothian. Much of an age with Telford, who describes him as a 'treasure of talents and integrity',[71] he had been brought to Shrewsbury by George Steuart in 1790 as clerk of works at St Chad's, to supersede Joseph Bromfield who had been dismissed.[72] His 'diligence, accuracy, and irreproachable integrity' were much to Telford's heart, and by 1798 he had 'all the works of any magnitude in this great and rich district'.[73] The dearth of well-trained master masons also brought Matthew Davidson down from Langholm in 1790 and after 1793 he quickly became canal mad.

As men of great practical curiosity William Reynolds and Telford must have been mutually attracted and were closely acquainted by 1795. His canal innovations were stoutly defended against the plagiarism of the American engineer, Charles Fulton, in Telford's article on canals written for Archdeacon Plymley in 1797, where he describes the east Shropshire canal system in detail and vindicates the priority of Salopian invention.[74] Together they probably made a lightning tour of the north and central Welsh mountains in 1797, which cannot have been entirely recreational.[75]

In more polite society Telford made an enduring friendship with Archibald Alison, author of the 'Essay on Taste', a fellow countryman, and another protégé of Pulteney. He was the first man to treat Telford as an equal and they had first met at Sudborough in 1784. From 1790 Alison was curate of Kenley, near Wenlock Edge, and subsequently rector of High Ercal and Rodington, before leaving for Edinburgh in 1800.[76] Telford was frequently at Kenley and later in Edinburgh, and intimate with the whole family. More influential, and on close terms with Alison, was Archdeacon Joseph Plymley, a model archdeacon, a leading magistrate, an ardent anti-slaver and a philanthropist. Telford worked for him and wrote the section on canals for Plymley's 'General View of the Agriculture of Salop' published in 1803. Telford was an acceptable house guest at Longnor and was held in high esteem by Catherine Plymley.

Most important of all, however, was William Pulteney, who had brought Telford to Shropshire. Despite Telford's evident abilities, Pulteney's support stood for something. It was through Pulteney that he was introduced to the British Fisheries Society and by this means brought to the attention of Sir John Sinclair for whom he wrote his treatise on mills. Pulteney and Telford 'quarrelled like tinkers', but despite the latter's initial political vagaries over Tom Paine they got on well together and Telford had a high admiration for him.

Conclusion

The pattern of Telford's life was well established by 1800. He had not only made his mark in Shropshire, but also in the metropolis, in Government circles and in Scotland. He was established as a leading civil engineer, as a man of integrity. He had already become a national figure and was soon to have an international reputation. He had a wide circle of friends, the ear of scientists, some powerful patrons, and had acquired the circle of trusted colleagues who were to work with him, supervise his works and execute his contracts.

As an engineer and administrator he had demonstrated his ability to supervise and execute complicated public works, travelling vast distances and working indefatigably under arduous conditions. He 'lived like a soldier always on active service'.[77] His life was all hurry and bustle:

> 'You know I am toss'd about like a Tennis Ball, the other day I was in London, since that I have been in Liverpool, and in a few days I expect to be in Bristol.'[78]

Increasingly he was to be away from Shropshire, and from 1807 at least he was conducting his duties as county surveyor by remote control through his deputy Thomas Stanton at Ellesmere.[79] Late in 1799 he compared himself to Napoleon 'fighting battles at 50 or 100 miles distance every other day. However plenty of employment is what every professional man is seeking after and mine require exertions – which it shall certainly have while I have health'.[80]

Acknowledgements

In writing this paper I am much indebted to Barrie Trinder, Alastair Penfold and Mrs M. Halford, and the staffs of the Shropshire County Record Office, the Local Studies Library, Shrewsbury, and the Ironbridge Gorge Museum Trust Library for bringing documents to my notice. Although I have tried to use as much new material as possible, I have inevitably drawn heavily on the biographies of Telford by Sir Alexander Gibb and L. T. C. Rolt.

References

Note: Where I have used letters written by Telford to Andrew Little I have generally used the text supplied by Gibb, but where letters have not been quoted in full, or have been used neither by Gibb nor Rolt, I have used Sir

Alexander Gibb's complete transcripts of the correspondence at the Iron-bridge Gorge Museum Trust Library.

1. Catherine Plymley's diary, 5 Nov., 1793. Shropshire County Record Office (SCRO), 1066/20.
2. Rickman, J. (ed). *Life of Thomas Telford*. London, 1838, 660.
3. Telford to Little, 27 Jan., 1787; Gibb, Sir A. *The story of Telford*. London, Alexander Mackhose, 1935, 18. (This letter has been severely bowdlerized in the text given by Gibb.)
4. Gibb, *ibid.*, 18; Shrewsbury Public Library, deeds 13571, 13572; bundle of plans and daybook in Telford's hand.
5. Colvin, H. M. *Biographical dictionary of architects, 1600–1846*. London, John Murray, 1978, 956.
6. *Shropshire Newsletter*, No. 44, 19–20; Shirehall and Gaol Commissioners minutes, f.38r. SCRO 348/10.
7. *Ibid.*; also Telford to Little, 21 Feb., 1788 (Gibb, *op. cit.*, 17–18).
8. Rickman, *op. cit.*, 25.
9. Gibb., *op. cit.*, 18.
10. Royal Salop Infirmary Minutes, vol. 1, 1 Sept., 1787; 16 Feb., 1788. SCRO.
11. Owen H. *Some account of the ancient and present state of Shrewsbury*. Shrewsbury, P. Sandford, 1808, 332.
12. Shrewsbury School Archives, Bailiff's accounts, vol. 2.
13. The account of the fall of St Chad's is based on Rickman, *op. cit.*, 26; Telford to Little, 16 July, 1788 (Gibb, *op. cit.*, 15); Owen H. and Blakeway J. B. *A history of Shrewsbury*. London, 1825, vol. 2, 245–248.
14. Owen and Blakeway, *op. cit.*, 298–300.
15. SCRO, 1041/Ch/71–72.
16. Shrewsbury School Archives, Bailiff's accounts, vol. 2.
17. Telford to Little, 3 Sept., 1788 (Gibb-Little transcripts, Ironbridge Gorge Museum Trust).
18. St Mary's Churchwardens' accounts. SCRO 1041/Ch5, 345, 346, 350.
19. *Ibid.*, 71–73.
20. *Ibid.*, 398.
21. *Orders of Salop Quarter Sessions*, 3, 37. SCRO.
22. Telford's statement of account to churchwardens, 30 May, 1791. SCRO 1580/1; also Cranage D. H. S. *An architectural account of the churches of Shropshire*. Wellington, Hobson, 1894–1912, 744–747.
23. Childe E. Cleobury Mortimer. *Trans Shrops. Archaeol. nat. Hist. Soc.*, ser. 1, 2, 54.
24. Telford to Little, 11 Mar., 1792 (Gibb-Little transcripts).

25. Rickman, *op, cit.*, 32.
26. Pevsner N. *Shropshire.* London, Penguin, 1958, 80.
27. Shrewsbury School Library, borrowing register, 1737–1820.
28. Description of plan of a church for Bridgnorth (Gibb-Little transcripts); also Rolt L. T. C. *Thomas Telford.* London, Longmans, 1958, 22–24.
29. *House of Commons Journals*, 47, 128.
30. Gibb-Little transcripts (see ref. 28.)
31. Telford to Little, 10 Mar., 1793 (Gibb-Little transcripts).
32. *Ibid.*
33. Shrewsbury Public Library, deed 15079B.
34. Shrewsbury School Archives, Kingsland House deeds.
35. *Victoria County History of Shropshire.* Oxford, 1979, vol. 3, 280–81; also Trinder B. S. *The Industrial Revolution in Shropshire.* Chichester, Phillimore, 1973, 298; also ex. inf. Dr H. M. Colvin.
36. Gibb, *op. cit.*, 18.
37. J. Bishton to Marquis of Stafford, 26 Mar., 1790. Staffordshire Records Office, D593/L/4/3. (Trinder, *op. cit.*, 81, mentions this possibility but Bishton's letter and memorandum make it clear that Telford was employed only in a subordinate capacity.)
38. Hill M. C. Iron and steel bridges in Shropshire, 1788–1901. *Trans. Shrops. Archaeol. nat. Hist. Soc.*, 1957–60, 56, 113.
39. Rickman, *op. cit.*, 27
40. Quarter Session files. SCRO, 8/138.
41. *Victoria County History of Shropshire.*, vol. 3, 127.
42. Telford to Little, 27 Jan., 1788 (Gibb., *op. cit.*, 14).
43. Telford to Little, 16 July, 1788 (Gibb., *op. cit.*, 19) Telford to Little, 3 Sept., 1788 (Gibb-Little transcripts), Also SCRO, 348/10, f. 45v; Rolt, *op. cit.*, 20.
44. Hill, *op. cit.*, 105; *Orders of Salop Quarter Sessions*, 3, 33.
45. Telford to Little, 8 Oct., 1789 (Gibb, *op. cit.*, 20).
46. Rickman, *op. cit.*, 27–28.
47. *Orders of Salop Quarter Sessions*, 3, 32–33. SCRO.
48. Ward A. W. *The bridges of Shrewsbury.* Shrewsbury, Wilding, 1935, 152–157.
49. Hadfield C. and Skempton A. W. *William Jessop, Engineer.* Newton Abbot, David & Charles, 1979, 141.
50. Rickman, *op. cit*, 34.
51. Telford to Little, 3 Nov., 1793 (Gibb, *op. cit.*, 22).
52. *Ibid.*
53. Shrewsbury Public Library, deed 15079B.
54. Telford to Little, 18 Mar., 1793 (Gibb, *op. cit.*, 22).

55. *Orders of Salop Quarter Sessions*, 3, 72–74.
56. Inscription on bridge.
57. Hill, *op. cit.*, 112.
58. Ruddock T. *Arch bridges and their builders, 1735–1835*. Cambridge, 1979, 149, 154; Telford to Little, 8 Dec., 1798 (Gibb, *op. cit.*, 39).
59. Hadfield and Skempton, *op. cit.*, 141–153.
60. Hill, *op. cit.*, 107.
61. Ruddock, *op. cit.*, 35–37.
62. Plymley H. *General view of the agriculture of Shropshire*. London, R. Phillips, 1803, 316.
63. Rickman, *op. cit.*, 29–30.
64. *Ibid.*, 682; also Cossons N. and Trinder B. *The iron bridge*. Bradford on Avon, Moonraker, 1979, 93.
65. Plymley, *op. cit.*, 300.
66. Cossons and Trinder, *op. cit.*, 89.
67. *Ibid.*, 93; also *Shropshire Newsletter*, No. 35, 1–6; also ex. inf. B. S. Trinder.
68. Telford to M. Davidson, 19 Feb., 1796. Davidson file, Ironbridge Gorge Museum Trust.
69. Cossons and Trinder, *op. cit.*, 93; Rickman, *op. cit.*, 682.
70. Shirehall and Gaol Commission minutes. SCRO, 348/10, f33v; 43v; *ibid.*, 228/6/95.
71. Telford to Little, 8 Dec., 1798 (Gibb., *op. cit.*, 39).
72. St Chad's Trustees minutes, 11 Mar., 1790. SCRO, 1048, Box 38.
73. Owen and Blakeway, *op. cit.*, vol. 2, 254; Telford to Little, 8 Dec., 1798 (Gibb, *op. cit.*, 39).
74. Plymley, *op. cit.*, 308.
75. Telford to Little, 20 Aug., 1797 (Gibb–Little transcripts); ex. inf. A. Penfold.
76. Sandford Rev. G. The early life of the historian Sir Archibald Alison, Bart. *Trans. Shrops. Archaeol. nat. Hist. Soc.*, − ser. 1, 7, 390–396.
77. Rickman, *op. cit.*, 283.
78. Telford to Little, 13 July, 1799 (Gibb, *op. cit.*, 41).
79. Telford to J. Loxdale, 10 Sept., 1807. SCRO 8/5.
80. Telford to Little, 30 Nov., 1799 (Gibb–Little transcripts).

~ 2 ~

The Shrewsbury and Newport Canals

Construction and remains

A. R. K. CLAYTON

When the idea of a canal to link the East Shropshire Coalfield with Shrewsbury was about to be put into practice, a network of over 20 miles of tub-boat canals had already been constructed linking various parts of the coalfield with the River Severn. The oldest was the Donnington Wood Canal, the main line of which was completed in 1768 from Pave Lane to Donnington Wood, where it later joined the short Wombridge Canal and the Shropshire Canal. The latter led to Oakengates and Coalport, with a branch to Coalbrookdale, and also linked with the Ketley Canal, on which was the first boat-carrying inclined plane to be constructed in the British Isles.

The Shrewsbury Canal (Fig. 1) has several features of particular interest, not the least of which is the fact that it is one of the first two canals with which Thomas Telford was associated. Furthermore, the tunnel, aqueducts, locks and inclined plane all have a significant place in the history of British canals.

History

In 1792, George Young surveyed the proposed Shrewsbury Canal. It was planned to run on the level for just over 12 miles from Shrewsbury, with aqueducts at Pimley, Rodington, and Longdon, and a tunnel near the village of Preston. It was then to climb about 79 ft in under 4 miles by means of eleven locks to Trench, where an inclined plane was to lift it up 75 ft to join the Wombridge Canal.

An Act was obtained in the following year, and the Committee lost no time in getting work under way. At the first meeting on 1 July, 1793, it was agreed that just over a mile of the Wombridge Canal should be purchased from William Reynolds, and on 6 July the contract for the construction of the first 10 040 yards at the eastern end was given to James Houghton, John Houghton and

23

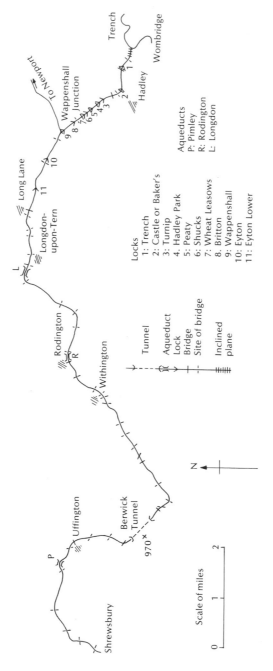

Fig. 1. Route of the Shrewsbury Canal

Thomas Ford. This length is almost certainly that up to Longdon Wharf from the top of Trench Incline. An unusual agreement mentioned in the minutes is that the pound above Eyton Lock should be constructed to a depth of 5 ft 6 in. in order that the miller at Eyton could draw up to 1 ft of water without inconveniencing the passage of boats.

An attempt to recruit the services of William Jessop or one of the Dadfords was unsuccessful, so in August Josiah Clowes was appointed as engineer under William Reynolds. In November the Committee was asking that the canal be completed to Long Lane by 1 January 1794, on which date the contract for the remaining length of the canal was awarded to the same team as before.

Late in 1794 Josiah Clowes died, and on 23 February, 1795, Thomas Telford, at that time engineer of the Ellesmere Canal under William Jessop, was asked to 'look at the aqueducts at Rodington and Longdon and the spot where Pimley Aqueduct was to be constructed'. Two days later he was appointed to replace Josiah Clowes, and was told to make a plan and estimate of alterations and additions to Longdon Aqueduct. A month later the plans for an iron aqueduct were approved, and the castings ordered. By November 1796 the works were finished, and the canal was opened throughout in February 1797.

The East Shropshire canal system remained isolated until 1835, when the construction of the 10½ mile long Newport Branch (Fig. 2) linked the Shrewsbury Canal at Wappenshall to the newly constructed Birmingham and Liverpool Junction Canal at Norbury. Nine years later both the Shrewsbury Canal and the Newport Branch became part of the Shropshire Union Railway and Canal Company.

In the latter part of the 19th century traffic declined, partially as a result of railway competition, and eventually Trench Incline and the canal above were closed in 1921. Shrewsbury Basin was closed the following year. The last traffic went up the locks to Trench in the 1930s, and that to Shrewsbury ceased in 1936. Coal traffic to Longdon Wharf ceased in 1939, and the last boat to reach Comet Bridge, near Shrewsbury, arrived late in 1940. The final traffic was on the branch to Newport, and the two canals were abandoned in 1944.

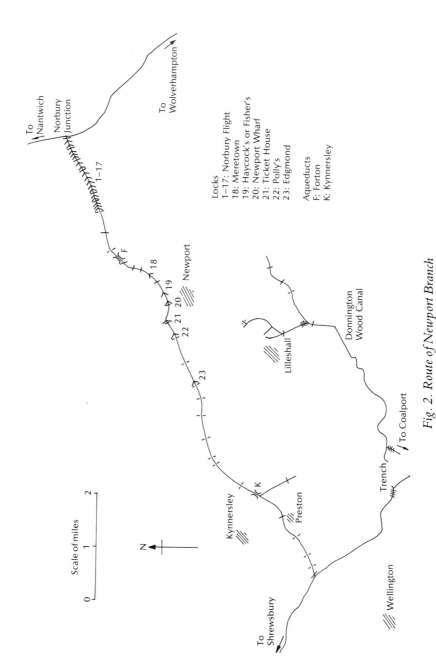

Locks
1–17: Norbury Flight
18: Meretown
19: Haycock's or Fisher's
20: Newport Wharf
21: Ticket House
22: Polly's
23: Edgmond

Aqueducts
F: Forton
K: Kynnersley

Fig. 2. Route of Newport Branch

Berwick Tunnel

This 970 yard long tunnel was designed by Josiah Clowes, who had earlier been the engineer in charge of the construction of the long Sapperton Tunnel on the Thames and Severn Canal. It was quite shallow, and it would probably have been built as a cutting a few years later. In July 1794 it was decided to build it wider than at first planned, and to construct a wooden towing-path through it. It was the first tunnel of any length to have a towpath, but this deteriorated with time, and was eventually removed in 1819.

The portals of the tunnel remain, although they are now bricked up for safety, along with the ventilation shafts (Fig. 3). The tunnel mouths were bell-shaped, so that the entrances appeared larger than the normal tunnel section. A curve in the tunnel meant that it was difficult to see through from one end to the other. The first hint of traffic regulation comes in 1838, when a committee meeting minuted that if two loaded trains of boats entered the tunnel at the same time, priority was to be given to the train reaching the centre of the tunnel first. It is said that a white line marked the mid-point. This unusual arrangement for the passage of boats must have proved very frustrating at times.

Fig. 3. Eastern portal of Berwick Tunnel, c. 1880 (Harry Arnold Collection)

Fig. 4. Rodington Aqueduct from the south (late 1960s) (Harry Arnold Collection)

The aqueducts

Pimley Aqueduct was a single-arched brick structure carrying the canal over a stream. The arch has since been removed, although the abutments remain and are linked by a modern footbridge. Although built after Josiah Clowes's death, there is no reason to suppose that his design was not used.

Rodington Aqueduct was a more substantial three-arched structure over the River Roden (Fig. 4). Made of brick, it also was designed by Clowes. The Roden at this point has a steep bank on the west side, but a considerable approach embankment was needed on the east side, through which a driving-way still survives. The main aqueduct was demolished in 1970.

Longdon Aqueduct still stands (Fig. 5) and has particular importance as it was the first major cast-iron canal aqueduct to be built, although a much smaller one on the Derby Canal was completed about a month earlier. With three slender cast-iron piers, the aqueduct spans 62 yds, and springs from brick and masonry abutments which themselves each contain two arches. The latter re-

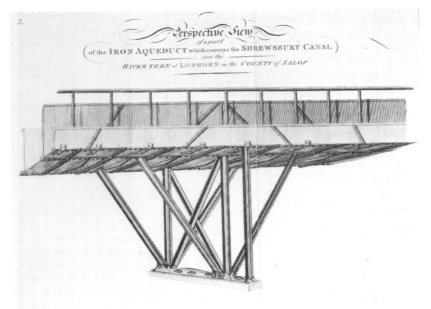

Fig. 5. Longdon Aqueduct (from Plymley) (Ironbridge Gorge Museum Trust)

semble those at Rodington, and thus seem almost certain to be part of Clowes's original aqueduct, which was severely damaged by floods early in 1795.

There has been some controversy as to whose idea it was to use cast iron. The Canal Company's minutes for 14 March, 1795, record that it was 'Ordered that an Iron Aqueduct be erected at Longdon (agreeable to a plan to be approved by Mr. Telford) by Messrs William Reynolds and Company', and in Plymley's *Shropshire* Telford later writes 'The idea of having this aqueduct made of cast-iron was first suggested by Thomas Eyton, Esq., then chairman of the committee'. However, in a letter to Andrew Little of Langholm dated 18 March, 1795, Telford wrote:

> 'I have just recommended an Iron Aqueduct for the most considerable. It is approved and will be executed under my direction upon a principle entirely new, and which I am endeavouring to establish with regard to the application of Iron'.

This evidence that the idea was Telford's is reinforced by a drawing of an iron canal aqueduct signed by Telford and dated March 1794 (Fig. 6). The dimensions on the drawing indicate that the design

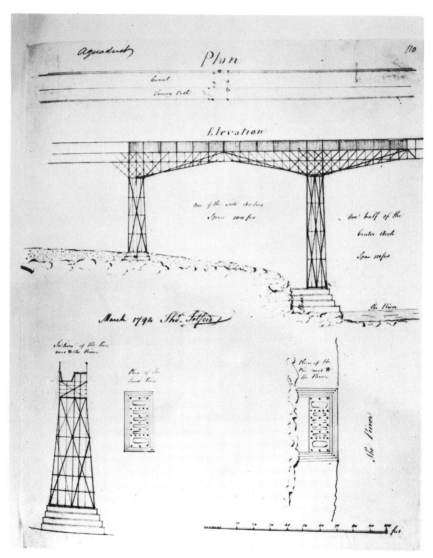

Fig. 6. Sketch of a proposed aqueduct by Thomas Telford (Ironbridge Gorge Museum Trust)

was for the crossing of the Dee at the present site of Pontcysyllte, but it nevertheless demonstrates that the idea of using iron for an aqueduct was being considered by him even at that early date. The Iron Bridge had been built only 16 years before, and cast-iron bridges were still relatively uncommon, so the use of this material by a trained stone mason seems unusual. However, it must be remembered that at the same time as Telford was faced with the problem of rebuilding Longdon Aqueduct, he also had to rebuild several bridges in Shropshire which had been washed away in the same year, and that he used cast iron for several of these. Combined with this was the availability of sufficient quantities of the new material close at hand in the industrial complex of East Shropshire.

The locks

There were eleven locks on the Shrewsbury Canal, all of which were unusual for narrow locks in the UK. They originally measured about 81 ft by 6 ft 7 in., being both longer and narrower than usual, and were designed to take up to four 20 ft by 6 ft tub-boats at a time. Details of the locks are given in Table 1.

Telford wrote about them in Plymley's *Shropshire*:

> ' – as small boats are used upon this canal the locks are so formed as to admit either one, three, or four boats passing at a time, without the loss of any more water than what is just necessary to regulate the ascent or descent of the boat or boats that are then in the locks. This is accomplished by having gates that are drawn up or let down perpendicularly instead of being worked horizontally, and each lock has three gates, one of which divides the body of the lock, so as to admit of one, three or four boats at a time'.

The locks as they are now, have conventional top gates and lifting gates at the lower end only. There is no record in the minute book or elsewhere of the intermediate gates being removed. However, in some of the locks there is possible evidence for their original presence. Just over 20 ft from the top gate sill, locks 4 and 6 show traces of grooves in the chamber walls below the original water-line, while in locks 10 and 11 there are vertical columns of bricks, as if such grooves had been infilled at a later date. However, to confirm whether or not these features do correspond to any former intermediate gates it would be necessary to excavate the lock chambers to see if there is a gate sill in the invert of the lock.

The use of vertically lifting, or 'guillotine' gates is unusual in narrow locks, and may have been for reasons of economy in the use of water. The minute book shows considerable concern over water supplies, and on 4 May, 1795, the Committee authorized the construction of a side-pound on a lock. This had been the idea of a John Price, and in September that year it was reported that two side-pounds had been made near Hadley. There is no further mention of this development, and no evidence for where they were built is to be found on the ground. It is possible that Baker's lock 2 was one of those involved, as later a wharf was constructed alongside it where a side-pound would have been.

In 1826 the Clerk of the proposed Birmingham and Liverpool Junction Canal attended the Annual General Meeting, and those present gave their assent to a branch canal to join the two waterways. As a consequence in 1831 the engineer, Henry Williams, was authorized to widen the locks and bridges between Wappenshall and Shrewsbury. This work was completed two years later at a cost of £1000 obtained on loan. The Newport Branch was opened to Newport on the 12 January 1835 and throughout seven weeks later. The consequent increase in trade enabled the Company to pay off the loan with interest before the Annual General Meeting the following October.

This left the nine locks between Trench and Wappenshall un-widened. In October 1836 the idea of widening them was considered but thought inexpedient as most trade came down the incline on tub-boats. The matter was brought up again in 1838, and this time it was considered that the extra income from enabling conventional narrow boats with their greater carrying capacity to work up to Trench would justify the expenditure. However, in July the engineer, John Beech, reported that the extra water required meant constructing a new reservoir, and the idea was dropped. Later specially designed Trench boats, 70 ft long but of low headroom and extra-narrow beam of 6 ft 2 in. were constructed for use on this section.

In 1840 it was found that some of the locks had to be repaired, and on 11 July the Committee minuted that 'The recommendation of Mr. Beech on the 9 May to adopt in repairing the 7th lock, a counterbalance of Cast Iron to work in a well, constructed at the back of the lock, instead of the old suspended counterbalance over

Table 1. Details of locks on Shrewsbury Canal

No.	Name	Type of lower gate*	Reconstruction date	Bridge at lock tail	Chamber	Top gate	Lower gate	Superstructure
1	Trench[1]	B	1841	Demolished	Demolished	1976	Absent	Absent
2	Baker's or Castle[2]	B	1841	Demolished	Intact	In situ	Skeletal	Present
3	Turnip	C	Unknown	No	Intact	Dam	Present	Present
4	Hadley Park	A		Present	Intact	Present	Absent	Absent (pit)
5	Peaty[3]	C	Unknown	Present	Intact	Dam	Absent	Absent (no pit)
6	Shucks[3]	A		No	Intact	Dam	Absent	Absent
7	Wheat Leasows[3]	B	1840	Present	Infilled	Dam	Absent	Present
8	Britton	C	1843	No	Half infilled	In situ	Absent	
9	Wappenshall[4]	C	1844	No	Demolished	Removed before 1969		
10	Eyton[5]	C	Unknown	No	Intact	Removed	Removed	Removed
11	Eyton Lower	A		No	Intact	Remains in situ	Present	Present

*A: Original design: wheel and axle lifting gear, counterbalance over tailbay.
B: First modification, 1840–41. wheel and axle lifting gear; counterbalance in pit alongside gate.
C: Second modification, 1843 on. Winch alongside gate. Counterbalance as for B.

Sources of information
1. Photograph in Hadfield. C. Canals of West Midlands.
2. Drawing: 'Bird's Eye View of Works at Hadley'. Salop County Record Office.
3. Photograph in collection of N. J. Clarke shows these three locks clearly (see Fig. 9).
4. Lifting gear stored by Ironbridge Gorge Museum Trust. A modern weir now stands on its site.
5. Converted into a weir. Lower gate and superstructure stored by Ironbridge Gorge Museum Trust. The top gate was removed to near lock 11 at the time of conversion.

the Tailbay, appearing to the Committee to be a decided improvement, Ordered that such an improvement be approved and sanctioned'. The minutes later record the repair of locks 1 and 2 in 1841, lock 8 in 1843 and lock 9 in 1844.

As shown in Table 1, only locks 4, 6 and 11 were not modified in this way (Fig. 7). A change in the lifting mechanism, with a marked change in the design of the superstructure, took place after the first three locks had been modified. The new style was much simpler in construction, and was probably easier to maintain (Fig. 8).

After abandonment in 1944 four of the locks had their gates removed and dams built across their forebays. Three of the locks have been demolished or infilled completely, while the remaining lock chambers survive in various states of repair. Full details are given in Table 1.

Some clearance work has recently been carried out in the area of Hadley Park Lock. This has reopened about 500 yards of towpath, and it is hoped that this may lead to eventual restoration of the lock as an operational museum piece.

Fig. 7. View of Hadleypark Lock, c. 1880 (Harry Arnold Collection)

Trench incline

The inclined plane at Trench connected the upper pound of the canal to the section of the Wombridge Canal bought from William Reynolds. It was 223 yds long with a vertical rise of 75 ft, a gradient of about 1 in 9. In its construction it was similar to those already built on the Shropshire Canal (Fig. 9). The original engine was built by the Coalbrookdale Company, as was its replacement, ordered in 1842. The rails were originally of cast iron on wooden sleepers, and apparently of U section. In 1839 the track was replaced using edge rails laid in chairs on stone sleepers, but more recent photographs show the track to be laid in standard railway fashion on wooden sleepers. A cast-iron aqueduct carried a feeder stream to Trench Reservoir across the lower end of the incline, and could still be seen before the construction of a new road in the vicinity, appearing as a trough at ground level.

The incline was the last canal incline to operate in the British Isles, closing in 1921. The last traffic was wheat to Donnington Wood Mill, which still stands.

Fig. 8. Peaty Lock, with Shucks Lock and Wheat Leasows Lock and lock cottage in background, c. 1943 (N. J. Clarke Collection)

Fig. 9. Trench Incline from below (Ironbridge Gorge Museum Trust)

The Newport Branch

The last canal project with which Telford was associated was the construction of the Birmingham and Liverpool Junction Canal. Work started in 1826, but the canal was not completed until after his death. Telford was also engineer to the Newport Branch, and the two canals are very similar in their type of construction and the design of their associated structures.

Wappenshall Junction grew to be an important transhipment centre, where goods were transferred from tub-boat to narrow boat, although tub-boats were used up the branch to Norbury and along the Main Line. A fine roving bridge is preserved as an ancient monument, and a well-designed warehouse still stands nearby with a short length of canal running underneath it, providing an extra link between the two canals (Fig. 10).

There were two major aqueducts on the branch. That at Kynnersley was a smaller and more ornate version of that which carries the Shropshire Union Main Line over the present A5 road at Stretton (Fig. 11). It carried the canal in a brick-lined trough enclosed in a cast-iron bridge over the Duke of Sutherland's drive linking Lille-

Fig. 10. Wappenshall Junction bridge and warehouse, 1977 (Author)

Fig. 11. Kynnersley Aqueduct shortly before demolition (Ironbridge Gorge Museum Trust)

shall with Kynnersley. Regrettably this delightful aqueduct, known to boatmen as the Little Aqueduct and embellished with stone carvings of the Duke of Sutherland's coat of arms, was demolished in the mid-1960s.

The other aqueduct at Forton is of very solid stone construction, with the canal being carried at full width over the River Meese by three skew arches (Fig. 12). The aqueduct also carries the Forton-Meretown road over the river on its northern side before it in turn crosses the canal by means of a very pronounced skew bridge.

The 23 locks were concentrated at the eastern end of the branch, 17 being concentrated in the Norbury Flight. These locks were of conventional design with mitred lower gates. The building of some of them in very peaty soil necessitated a considerable batter in the walls, making those locks wider at the upper water-level than at the lower. This was particularly pronounced at Edgmond Lock, the lowest on the canal.

A short branch canal ¾ mile in length left the Newport Branch just south of Kynnersley Aqueduct. This was constructed at a later date and led to Lubstree Wharf, which opened in 1844. The branch became known as the Humber Arm, and after 1870 a railway led from the wharf to the Lilleshall Company's works, thus avoiding the necessity for goods to traverse the incline and nine locks down

Fig. 12. Forton Aqueduct from the south, 1977 (Author)

to Wappenshall. A transhipment building still survives, along with a short section of canal in water, although most of the arm is dry. Near the junction can be found the remains of a wooden tub-boat, now in a poor state. It was last used as a maintenance boat, and traces of a roofed cabin are visible at one end.

Four lock cottages survive on the Newport Branch (Fig. 13). These are typical of Telford's design, and show a remarkable similarity to the toll-houses found along the Holyhead Road.

Conclusion

It can be seen that the appointment of Telford as engineer late in the construction of the Shrewsbury Canal meant that his influence in its design was minor, with the one exception of Longdon Aqueduct. The locks and incline had almost certainly been completed by the end of 1794, and construction of the tunnel was well under way. The enigma provided by his mention of intermediate gates in the locks remains unsolved, and can probably only clarified by excavation.

However, there is little doubt that Telford's experience on the Shrewsbury Canal in general, and the Longdon Aqueduct in particular, provided an important foundation for his more famous canal structures at Chirk and Pontcysyllte, and helped to establish

Fig. 13. Haycocks's Lock Cottage

his reputation as one of the country's leading canal engineers.

In contrast to the Shrewbury Canal, the Newport Branch bears all the hallmarks of Telford's influence, from the characteristic lock cottages to the design of the bridges.

Bibliography

Bracegirdle B and Miles P. H. *Thomas Telford.* Newton Abbot, David & Charles, 1973

Hadfield C. *The canals of the West Midlands.* Newton Abbot, David & Charles, 1969.

Howard Williams, W. The canal system of East Shropshire. *Shropshire Magazine,* May-August, 1954.

Plymley J. *A general view of the agriculture of Shropshire.* London, R. Phillips, 1803

Shrewsbury Canal Company. Minute Book.

Trinder B. S. *The industrial revolution in Shropshire.* Chichester, Phillimore, 1973.

~ 3 ~

The Holyhead Road

An engineering project in its social context

BARRIE TRINDER

'This road', wrote Thomas Telford towards the end of his life, 'established through a rugged and mountainous district, partly along the slope of rocky precipices, and across inlets of the sea, where the mail and other coaches are now enabled to travel at the rate of nine or ten miles an hour, was indeed an arduous undertaking, which occupied fifteen years of incessant exertion'.[1] An itinerary of the Holyhead Road is a catalogue of major works of engineering: Chirk embankment, the Glyn Diffwys pass, the Waterloo Bridge, the road through Nant Ffrancon, the Menai Bridge, the new road across Anglesey, the Stanley Embankment comprise a record of achievement which would have satisfied many engineers who did nothing else. One of Telford's obituarists considered that 'he was inclined to set a higher value on the success which attended his exertions for improving the great communication from London to Holyhead, the alterations of the line of road, its smoothness, and the excellence of the bridges, than on the success of any other work he executed'.[2] Yet, like all great engineering projects, the Holyhead Road was not just the isolated achievement of an individual, but a project which was shaped by a diversity of social and economic pressures, which grew out of particular social circumstances, and which had important micro-economic consequences. It is the purpose of this paper to set the Holyhead Road in its historical context, and to analyse both those factors which shaped the project, and the consequences of the construction of what was probably the best road in Europe of its date.

The impetus

In an important article published in 1964,[3] Mervyn Hughes drew attention both to the administrative novelty of the Holyhead Road

41

project, and to the importance of the role of Sir Henry Parnell, MP
for Queen's County, in the work of the Holyhead Road Commission. The Act of Union between the parliaments of England and
Ireland in 1800 naturally increased traffic between London and
Dublin, and drew the attention of the political nation to the poor
state of road communication between the two capitals. In Telford's
words, it 'produced constant irritation and complaints respecting
the road through North Wales and gave rise to warm discussions in
Parliament'.[4] In 1801 Joseph Huddard and John Rennie were
instructed to investigate the routes between the two cities, and to
make recommendations for improvements, but nothing came of
their work. In March 1810 a parliamentary committee was appointed to inquire into the road, and it was through this committee that
Thomas Telford, 'an engineer of great eminence'[5] as it called him,
first became concerned with the project. Telford prepared a
thorough and melancholy report on the road, but it was not until
1815 that the Holyhead Road Commission was constituted.[6]

Most main roads in England and Wales were administered in the
early 19th century by turnpike trusts, who had to raise money for
improvement through loans secured on the future income from
tolls. Such trusts were 17th-century expedients for transferring the
costs of maintenance to road users from those who lived alongside
main roads. The Holyhead Road Commission was empowered to
spend considerable sums of government money on the improvement of the road, the costs of which could never have been covered
by the limited revenue raised by tolls in the remote mountains of
North Wales, where there was little traffic other than long-distance
stage and posting coaches.

By 1815, as a result of Telford's report of 1810, it was accepted
that the route to be improved should be that through Shrewsbury,
Llangollen and across Snowdonia. Telford and the Commissioners
doubted the capacity of the existing turnpike trusts to maintain the
road adequately once improvements had been carried out, and in
1819 an Act was obtained setting up a new Parliamentary Turnpike
Commission,[7] which took over responsibility for the maintenance
of the road west of Shrewsbury from the six turnpike trusts which
had previously administered it. Several members of the new Commission also sat on the Holyhead Road Improvement Commission
of 1815, and the two bodies worked closely together, both report-

ing annually to Parliament. The Commission of 1819 was conceived by Sir Henry Parnell as a 'new model' turnpike trust, differing from existing trusts in its direct responsibility to Parliament, in its small but able and active membership, and in its commitment to ensure that the road was administered by experienced and qualified engineers.[8]

A second Act of Parliament of 1819[9] authorized the building of the Menai and Conway suspension bridges and a completely new road across the island of Anglesey. An Act of 1820 renewed the powers of the original commission, especially as far as the English portion of the road was concerned.[10] In 1824 the two suspension bridges were vested with the commission, and further expenditure on the road was authorized.[11] Several subsequent acts increased the amounts available for improvements, and by 1830 the commissioners under the Act of 1815 had spent over £750 000 in government grants and loans on the improvement of the road.[12]

Route

In the mid-18th century the choice of the route from London to Holyhead through Shrewsbury, Llangollen, Bettws-y-coed and Capel Curig would have seemed surprising. Travellers to Dublin, if they did not go through South Wales, usually took the ancient Chester Road, turnpiked from Stonebridge, Warwickshire, to Chester in 1760, and then went along the coast of North Wales, crossing the Conway estuary and the Menai Straits by ferries. That Shrewsbury became an important staging point on the route to Holyhead was due to the initiative of Robert Lawrence, an innkeeper in the town.[13] The promotion of the route to Ireland was one feature of an extraordinary flowering of talents in Shrewsbury in the last two decades of the 18th century, a period which saw the restoration of the academic reputation of Shrewsbury Schools under Samuel Butler, the construction of the world's first multi-storied iron-framed building to the design of Charles Bage, several ambitious building projects designed to make Shrewsbury a town of resort, and the beginnings of William Hazledine's great coal and ironworking concerns. The recorder of this renaissance was Catherine Plymley, sister of Archdeacon Joseph Plymley of Longnor Hall, author of *The general view of the agriculture of Shropshire,*[14] which incorporated contributions by several of the most talented

Salopians of the period. Catherine Plymley's diaries record her
brother's constant contacts with such people as the ironmasters
Richard and William Reynolds, the anti-slavery agitator Thomas
Clarkson, the philosopher Archibald Alison, and with Thomas
Telford, whom she met at Longnor after attending a performance
by Sarah Siddons at the theatre in Shrewsbury in 1793.[15]

When Telford conducted his enquiry into the Holyhead Road in
1810 he was instructed to investigate the various routes between
London and Dublin 'without regard to special interests'[16] Doubt-
less, as a highly scrupulous and professional engineer he did so. But
he cannot, as a member of the talented elite which flourished in
Shrewsbury in the 1790s, have been unaware of the extent to which
the Irish thoroughfare trade had grown in the town, and how this
had been as much the outcome of entrepreneurial zeal as the development of the flax-spinning industry or of iron-founding.

It was in 1779, the year in which the Iron Bridge was constructed, that the promotion of the route from Shrewsbury to Holyhead
began (Fig. 1). In April, the 'New Company', a consortium of innkeepers formed to improve travel in North Wales, fixed standard
rates for post chaise travel on the route from Shrewsbury to Holyhead through Oswestry, Llangollen, Ruthin, St Asaph and
Conway. The rates, 9*d* a mile with a pair, and 1*s* 3*d* a mile with a
four, were the same as on most English roads.[17] In May 1779
Robert Lawrence, then landlord of the Raven and Bell inn, which
stood adjacent to the Lion at the top of Wyle Cop in Shrewsbury,
began a stage coach service to Holyhead through Ellesmere, Wrex-
ham, Mold and Conway, with three departures a week, the service
taking 36 hours, and carrying four passengers.[18] The following
summer he began a second service, through Oswestry, Llangollen,
Corwen and Llanrwst, on alternating days, giving six departures a
week to Holyhead.[19] On 1 January, 1781, he moved to the Lion
Hotel,[20] a magnificent building erected by the astute attorney John
Ashby, and the acknowledged centre of Shropshire society.[21] His
coach services were transferred to the Lion with him.

Within a few years the Holyhead service was well established,
and in 1785 a consortium of turnpike trusts published a table point-
ing out how distances had been reduced and steep hills avoided by
improvement schemes which they had carried out.[22] The route still
posed many problems, however, and in 1786 a directory noted that

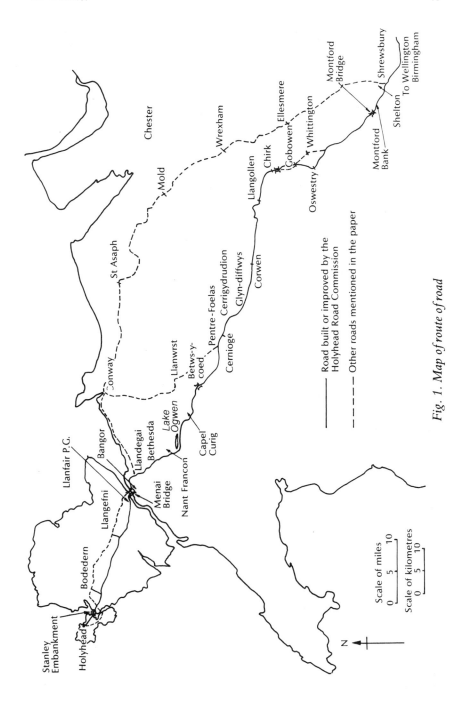

Fig. 1. Map of route of road

the arrival time in Shrewsbury of the Holyhead coach was 'uncertain'.[23] By the mid-1780s Lawrence's services were rivalled by coaches promoted by his successor at the Raven and Bell.[24] Both inns offered connections between their Holyhead coaches and services to London, and to Bath and Bristol. Advertisements drew attention to the romantic scenery, promising 'a great variety of beautiful cascades and pleasing prospects', as well as the avoidance of the 'dangerous and disagreeable ferry at Conway,'[25] which was ensured by crossing the River Conway at Llanrwst. By 1791, when the erection of a new Welsh Bridge in Shrewsbury was in prospect, it was hailed as the forerunner of other improvements in the town, which were much to be wished, 'there being now so much travelling on that road'.[26] The author of a directory in 1803 noted:

> 'of late years this town has been a principal thoroughfare between London, Birmingham, Bristol and Dublin; through the perseverance of Mr. Lawrence of this town the road from hence to Holyhead is not only much shortened but made most agreeably convenient'.[27]

In 1802, due in part to the efforts of Lawrence, parliamentary sanction was obtained for a new turnpike road from Bangor Ferry via Capel Curig to Pentre Foelas, which was opened to traffic in the autumn of 1804, reducing the distance from Shrewsbury to Holyhead by 9 miles.[28] Robert Lawrence died in 1804, but the coach services from the Lion were maintained by his brother John, and the route to Holyhead gradually assumed greater importance. On Tuesday, 6 September, 1808, the Irish mails for the first time travelled from London to Dublin through Shrewsbury, bringing great advantages to the country town through the earlier arrival of its own letters from the capital.[29]

The effects of a new route were felt in the remotest parts of the mountainous areas through which it passed. A traveller across the watershed between the Dee and the Conway in 1805 noted:

> 'As this is the great Irish road, the constant sight of strangers passing and re-passing gives the natives a considerable share of assurance, and a habit of mendicity which we had seldom witnessed in Wales'.[30]

New inns were opened to cater for the growing traffic. When the act for the Capel Curig road was obtained, Rhydllanfair House was offered to let for an inn. Such inns were badly needed.[31] A traveller in Llangollen in 1805 found that because the town was one of the regular stages on the Irish road, the inn:

> 'seems in a continual bustle . . . it would be a profitable speculation for
> an individual, and a benefit to the public, to erect another inn. The Bon-
> iface of the present would likewise gain in manners what he might lose
> in money'.[32]

Competition for stage coach traffic continued to be fierce. By
1815 there were day and night services from the Lion to Holyhead,
as well as the Royal Mail, and rival coaches from the Talbot.[33] In
August 1815 the Mail was taking 41 hours to travel the 276 miles
from London to Holyhead through Oxford, Birmingham and
Shrewsbury.[34]

Welsh section

In spite of Lawrence's enterprise, the road through Wales was
well below the standards of the better roads of the time. Nor was
this surprising, for from a point west of Corwen, where it climbed
out of the Dee valley, across the grim marshes which form the
watershed between the Dee and the Conway, and again through
the mountains between the crossing of the Conway at Bettws-y-
coed and Bangor, there was little local traffic to boost the toll
income which came from the stage and post coaches taking passengers to Ireland. No road in such an area could be expected to gen-
erate sufficient income in tolls to provide capital for adequate
routine maintenance, still less for major improvements. Telford
found that on the 85 days between 1 January and 27 March, 1810,
the Shrewsbury–Holyhead Mail was between 1 and 5 hours late on
71 occasions, and in the reverse direction it was punctual on only 10
days. During 1809 there were six major breakdowns. On one oc-
casion the coach overturned near Corwen. Once a spring broke,
and there were four incidents when shackles broke. It was with no
exaggeration that Telford referred in the first report of the 1815
Commission, to 'the extreme danger to which everyone who travelled this road was exposed'.[35]

In 1824 Telford stated that his objective in improving the Holyhead Road was 'that horses may easily and rapidly trot over the
whole road, ascending or descending, with a loaded coach', maintaining an average speed of 8 miles/h. Ideally there were to be no
gradients steeper than 1 in 30, although in practice some steeper

Fig. 2 'Depot' for road metals at Bettws-y-coed (Ironbridge Gorge Museum Trust)

sections remained. The average width of the road was to be 40 ft, and it was never to be narrower than 30 ft, with an 18 ft minimum of gravelled surface in the centre. Close attention was given to side and cross drains, and footpaths were built on many sections, ideally on the south side, so that the carriageway would gain maximum benefit from the drying action of the sunlight. For reasons of visibility and drainage, overhanging trees were felled, and where possible roadside hedges were replaced by stone walls.[36] Most of the walls were originally in dry stone, but the majority were mortared during the 1830s because the Welsh had constantly pilfered building materials from them.[37] In mountainous country the road was lined with parapet walls, matched by massive retaining walls securing the road from landslips.[38] Depots or recesses (Fig. 2) were built at regular intervals for the storage of road metals.[39]

Work on the road began in the autumn of 1815. One of the first major sections to be improved was that from Bettws-y-coed across the River Conway, and along the 3 mile face of Dinas Hill to Rhydllanfair, which Telford regarded as the most dangerous part of the whole route from Shrewsbury to Holyhead.[40] This improvement included the construction of the spectacular Waterloo Bridge over the Conway, with roses, thistles, leeks and shamrocks cast in the spandrels (Fig. 3), but the well-known inscription on the bridge, claiming that it was built in the year the Battle of Waterloo was fought, is erroneous. As late as 7 August, 1816, a Shrewsbury newspaper reported that the skeleton pieces for the iron bridge over the Conway at Bettws had been shipped from Chester for their destination the previous week.[41] The other major section to be completed within the first 2 years of work was that from the summit at the west end of Lake Ogwen, 993 ft above sea level, to Ty-Gwyn, previously one of the most difficult sections on the road, where, Telford noted with disgust, passengers in coaches had been in the habit of amusing themselves by throwing coping stones from the parapet into the valley below as they walked up the gradient behind their empty coaches. 'The most dreadful horsepath in Wales' became within 2 years 'an arduous and very expensive work ... which may be expected, with reasonable attention, to endure for ages'. Other improvements completed during the Commission's first 2 years included the road from Bangor Ferry to Bangor, which was lowered by 90 ft, that from Rhydllanfair to Glan Conway,

Fig. 3. Waterloo Bridge

which avoided several steep hills, and the 780 yd by-pass around the village of Cerrig-y-Druidon, a section which still has a raw, newly-built air about it.[42]

By 1819 Telford was able to report that a new road, 2 miles 731 yd long, had been constructed through the rocky pass of Glyn Diffwys, through which travellers climbed from the Dee Valley to the high marshy table-land which forms the watershed between the Dee and the Conway. Just before the work began, in the autumn of 1816, the Mail overturned in the pass while rounding an acute bend: the luggage from the top of the coach hurtled into an abyss 100 ft below, the coachman broke his leg, and the guard only just escaped the fate of the luggage. Any outside passengers would certainly have been killed. Although less well-known than the road in the pass of Nant Ffrancon, the Glyn Diffwys pass remains a work which is breathtakingly daring, and one of the outstanding sections of the Holyhead Road.[43]

During 1819 work was in progress in the lower end of the Nant Ffrancon pass, and on a 4¼ mile section between Capel Cerig and Lake Ogwen, where Telford relocated the road to run on the north side of the valley of the Llugwy, where it was exposed to the drying action of the sun, instead of on the south side, where the route of the Bangor-Pentrefoelas turnpike had run. In the next 3 years further work was done in Nant Ffrancon, between Corwen and Llangollen, and through the streets of the latter town. By 1822 projects were under way between Pontcysyllte and Chirk, and between Cernioge and Cerrig-y-Druidon, where the road across the bogs was in places so narrow that coaches could not pass each other.[44]

In the spring of 1822 a completely new road, 18 miles long, was completed across the island of Anglesey, avoiding the principal settlements but with branch roads to Bodedern and Llangefni. In the summer of 1823 the new route across the island assumed its final form with the completion of the Stanley Embankment across the channel between Holy Island and Anglesey proper. The embankment is 1300 yd long and 16 ft high, and was one of the principal engineering works on the road (Fig. 4). Another completely new section of road was that between Gobowen and Chirk, which was finished in 1824–25. The massive embankment by which the road climbs from the bridge over the Ceiriog to the vil-

Fig. 4. Milestone at western end of Stanley Embankment, Anglesey (Ironbridge Gorge Museum Trust)

lage of Chirk had been completed by the spring of 1824 when trees were being planted to stabilise the slopes.[45] By 1825 Telford was able to speak of 'the present perfect state of the road' and to claim that 'from Chirk to Holyhead, a distance of 83 miles, the whole road is perfectly hard, smooth and clean, notwithstanding the very unfavourable weather for roads that is just over'.[46] His claim had even more validity the following year when, on 30 January, 1826, the suspension bridge over the Menai Straits was opened.[47] It was with some apparent satisfaction that Telford wrote during that year that:

> 'this great length of road in North Wales continues to be maintained by the Commissioners in a perfect state, and the merits of the substantial plan on which it has been constructed become every year more apparent'.[48]

In 1827 he was able to report that:

> 'from Chirk, along the Parliamentary Road to Holyhead, the surface of the road is uniformly hard and smooth, constant attention being bestowed in maintaining it in perfect order'.

The Menai Bridge, he wrote:

> 'has now been travelled upon for more than twelve months, without obstacle or interruption, and the public have acquired a perfect confidence in its stability'.[49]

   Improvements of the road west of Chirk after the completion of
the Menai Bridge were mostly of a minor character, the most important being the straightening of the routes through the towns of
Llangollen and Corwen.

English section

   The road between Shrewsbury and the Welsh border at Chirk
remained deficient, probably because Telford had long contempla-
ted a direct route from Wellington to Chirk, avoiding the county
town, but gradually it was improved. In 1824 Telford turned to the
traffic problems of Shrewsbury itself:

> 'The peninsular form' he wrote, 'which being well adapted for defence
> was its original recommendation, and which still constitutes much of
> its picturesque beauty, is rather inconvenient as regards its approaches,
> and this inconvenience is still further increased by the shape of the
> ground, which consists of a ridge of considerable elevation, with bold
> and steep banks facing the river, renders it singularly difficult to acquire
> a commodious thoroughfare for wheel carriages without destroying
> much valuable property, and otherwise incurring a very heavy
> expense'.

   Telford suggested two drastic proposals for creating a new route
between the two Severn bridges.[50] Neither was adopted, but the
threat seems to have had the effect of stimulating the citizens of the
county town to improve the existing route by laying new surfaces
and straightening building lines. Proposals were made for improving the routes through the suburbs, and these were gradually
implemented, the most important work being the cutting near the
house called The Mount, occupied by the Darwin family. Other
improvements between Shrewsbury and Gobowen were slowly
completed, but the most important scheme on that section, the
road over Montford Bank, just west of Shrewsbury, was not completed until after Telford's death.
   The route of the Holyhead Road from London to Shrewsbury
was fixed in 1817 when W. A. Provis recommended the road
through Coventry to Birmingham, and thence via Wolverhampton and Shifnal, largely because its southern section was already
much used as the principal route to Manchester and Liverpool, and
was therefore in good condition.[51] The improvement of the route
east of Shrewsbury was carried out by the local turnpike trusts in

collaboration with the Holyhead Road Commission of 1815, which arranged finance through government loans. While Telford and his assistants regularly reported on the upkeep of the road, they did not enjoy, under the Act of 1815, the total power which they were able to exercise west of Shrewsbury under the 1819 Act.

Work in England did not begin until 1819. For a long time improvement was inhibited by ambitious plans for totally new, more direct roads, avoiding congested area, in particular proposals for new sections from Stonebridge to Moxley, by-passing Birmingham, and from Wellington to Chirk, avoiding Shrewsbury and Oswestry.[52] Both schemes were fiercely opposed by the tradesmen of the towns concerned. The Wellington-Chirk scheme was advocated by Telford in 1822, and he still supported it in March 1830, when he suggested that its eastern terminus should be the north western end of the great Ketley embankment, instead of at the Cock Inn, and pointed out that it would save four crossings of the Severn, the 'inconveniently steep and awkward streets of the town of Shrewsbury', and two major hills at Montford and Overley.[53] He still advocated the road in 1833.

The proposal was never accepted however, and gradually during the 1820s and 30s the improvements which it had delayed were carried into effect. By 1830 almost the whole of the portion of the Holyhead Road in the care of the trustees of the Shifnal division of the Watling Street trust was rebuilt, with a new road in the centre of Shifnal, and a completely new section between Knowle Bank and the Greyhound Inn, Oakengates. A massive embankment was constructed across the valley of the Ketley Brook outside Wellington. By the time of Telford's death the extensive Overley Hill scheme west of Wellington, stretching from Burcote almost to the Horseshoe Inn at Uckington, was under way, and it was opened in December 1835. In 1837 work began on Montford Bank west of Shrewsbury. By 1834 a new road through Wolverhampton was finished and in perfect order, and by April 1837 a new road to the south of the Abbey Church in Shrewsbury was opened, avoiding the old circuitous route round the church.

From 1825 the Holyhead Road Commission was also involved in a series of improvements to the road along the coast of North Wales from Chester to the road from Shrewsbury at Llandegai outside Bangor. Principal among these were the Conway suspension bridge, opened in the summer of 1826, and the roads around Penmaen Mawr and Penmaen Bach, but this section was never treated with the thoroughness applied to the Holyhead Road proper.[54]

Road furniture

The Holyhead Road was constructed with a panache and a feeling for the dramatic equalled on no other road in England. At the very beginning of the project there was great pride in the victory of Waterloo. Telford said of the Conway Bridge at Bettws that 'having the national emblems, the rose, the thistle, the shamrock and the leek in the angles, it becomes a public and lasting testimonial of the action which so splendidly terminated the war.[55] As work on the road commenced, one of the chief contractors, John Straphen, was largely responsible for the construction of columns alongside it, one at Shrewsbury and one at Llanfair P.G., commemorating Lord Hill and the Marquess of Anglesey, two of the

Fig. 5. Milestone near Dinas Hill (Ironbridge Gorge Museum Trust)

Fig. 6. Tollhouse at Ty-issa near Llangollen

Fig. 7. Tollhouse at Caergaliog, Anglesey (Ironbridge Gorge Museum Trust)

heroes of the battle.[56] The whole length of the road from Shrewsbury to Holyhead was supplied with new milestones in 1826–28. (Fig. 5). They were quarried from near Red Wharf Bay on the coast of Anglesey, and cost £5 each to install. They were carved from a fine, hard limestone, a type of marble, with a total height of 4 ft 6 in. of which about 2 ft appeared above the ground. They weighed 23 cwt each. Telford justified the expense on the ground that most existing milestones were illegible and useless, commenting:

> 'I never saw a proper milestone that I could copy. I looked for three years all over England trying to find out one as a pattern, and after all I could not find one that looked like a decent milestone'.[57]

Fifteen tollhouses of standard patterns were also built between Shrewsbury and Holyhead, four room bungalows on the mainland (Fig. 6), and houses with three ground floor rooms and a tower bedroom on Anglesey (Fig. 7). Telford considered that such comfortable houses enabled the road authorities to get respectable people to collect the tolls, which greatly augmented their income. Sir Henry Parnell later wrote that tolls often increased when good toll houses were provided on a road, and quoted the house from Shelton on the Holyhead Road, now preserved in the Blists Hill Open Air Museum, as an example of excellence.[58] Gates of standard patterns were provided at the tollhouses, sometimes of stout woodwork, constructed on a lattice pattern, and sometimes of wrought iron in the familiar rising sun design.

Effects of the road

The object of the Holyhead Road Commission was to improve communication between London and Dublin. In the space of 16 years, as a result of the Commission's work, the time for the Royal Mail between London and Holyhead was reduced from 41 hours to 28, a reduction of over 30%.[59] It is impossible to quantify the economic significance of this reduction, to assess how much extra traffic was generated, how much time was saved by those making the journey, what traffic was diverted from other routes, or what additional goods were carried. It is clear nevertheless that the manifest purpose of the Commission was fulfilled, and that its economic consequences must have been considerable.

The improvement of the road also had many economic side

effects. It proved of considerable importance in the heavy industrial areas of the Black Country and the Coalbrookdale coalfield. It was of especial importance to the coalfield around Chirk, where coal carts made much use of the road and considerably damaged it. Toll houses and bars were relocated to ensure that the payments made were commensurate with the damage they caused. The coal traffic affected an area from Oswestry, where carts going to and from the great lime rocks at Llanymynech came on to the road, through Gobowen, Chirk, Vron and Llangollen, to the junction with the Bala road west of Corwen.[60] The road also stimulated production in the collieries on Maltreath Marsh on Anglesey, traffic from which was reported to be damaging the road in 1841.[61] The road from Bethesda to Bangor and Port Penrhyn was used by increasing numbers of slate carts in the late 1830s.[62]

Throughout its length the Holyhead Road stimulated the production of roadstone quarries. Telford insisted on the use of good quality stone, which created a considerable demand for the produce of such quarries as those on the Breiddens or Overley Hill. One strange consequence of the opening of the Menai Bridge seems to have been to stimulate the import of Irish pigs on the hoof. In 1826 the commissioners found it necessary to build low walls to protect the roots of hedges between the bridge and Bangor from the burrowing snouts of pigs being driven along the road.[63] A final and ironic economic consequence of the building of the road was that it enabled the building of the railways which robbed it of its traffic to be carried out more quickly. In the late 1840s the reports on the road mention the carriage of construction materials for railways in several areas.[64]

Conclusion

The Holyhead Road had a very short life as a major means of transport. The opening of the Menai Bridge in 1826 may be considered to mark the completion of the Welsh portion of the road, but in England several major long-awaited projects had still to be started when Telford died in 1834. The same report which mentioned the completion of Montford Bank noted that the opening of the London and Birmingham and Grand Junction railways had attracted away most of the posting traffic, the most profitable on the road, and that the only stage coach between Shrewsbury and

Holyhead had been withdrawn, leaving the Royal Mail as the only regular public communication over the western portion of the road.

The Commission reported in 1839 that railways had not injured the turnpike trusts, but that they had totally destroyed the value of the property of innkeepers, coach proprietors and others who had catered for long distance travellers. While on the lowland portion of the route local traffic remained heavy, on the Menai Bridge–Cernioge section there had never been much, apart from the long distance coaches, and since these had fallen off, toll income was inadequate to sustain the cost of maintenance. It was proposed in 1839 to lay a plateway along the road from Birmingham to London.[65]

A new day mail route to Dublin using the railway between Birmingham and Hartford (Cheshire) was opened in 1837, taking 26 hours, instead of the 28 taken by coaches on the Holyhead Road.[66] With the opening of the London and Birmingham Railway in 1838, and of the Chester and Holyhead in 1850, this time was dramatically cut. The Shropshire portion of the road lost its remaining long and medium distance traffic in 1849 with the opening of the Shrewsbury and Birmingham Railway, an event vividly remembered by the man who at the time was toll collector at Burcote:

'this was the cause of removing nearly all the traffic from the Turnpike trusts as if by magic . . . and the road that was considered the best in England, namely London to Holyhead, in a few months time was almost deserted, and is so up to this day'.[67]

In 1851 the surveyors for the Commission found grass encroaching on the road in Anglesey, and it was not surprising that the Commissioners concluded in their 28th report:

'We are of the opinion that the road is no longer of such national importance as to justify us in applying to Parliament for a grant of public money for its future maintenance'.[68]

Telford's road was a long-lasting memorial to his skill and vision. It is only in the late 1960s and 1970s that major attempts have been made to improve its line. All but about a dozen of the 106 milestones between Shrewsbury and Holyhead are still standing, although some have lost their inscribed cast-iron plates. Eleven

Telford tollhouses still stand on the same section of road, to which may be added the Shelton tollhouse preserved at the Blists Hill Open Air Museum, several constructed by the various turnpike trusts which do not conform to the standard Telford patterns, and several tollhouses east of Shrewsbury designed by Telford, but not to the standard patterns used on the Parliamentary Road. The bridges, while today mostly sustained by steel and concrete rather than by stonework, wrought iron and cast iron, still retain their original appearance.

The road remains an impressive record of the uncommon genius who created it and of Sir Robert Parnell whose parliamentary skills made it possible, but also of the ironfounder William Hazledine, the stone mason John Straphen and the coach operator Robert Lawrence, and of the whole of that brilliantly talented society which for a short time at the end of the 18th century flourished in Shrewsbury.

References
1. Rickman J. (ed). *Life of Thomas Telford*. London, 1838, 213.
2. *Annual Register*, 1834, 237.
3. Hughes M. Telford, Parnell and the Great Irish Road. *J. Transp. Hist.*, 1964, 4, 199–209.
4. Rickman, *op. cit.*, 206.
5. 3rd report from Commissioners on Holyhead Roads and Harbour. British Parliamentary Papers (BPP), 1811.
6. Acts of Parliament. 55. Geo. III, c. 152, 1815.
7. *Ibid.* 59 Geo. III, c. 30, 1819.
8. Hughes, *op. cit.*, 205–206.
9. Acts of Parliament. 59 Geo. III, c. 48, 1819.
10. *Ibid.*, 1 Geo. IV, c. 70, 1820.
11. *Ibid.*, 4 Geo. IV, c. 78, 1824.
12. Report of Select Committee on Holyhead and Liverpool Roads. BPP, 1830, 10.
13. Owen H. and Blakeway J. B. *A history of Shrewsbury*. London, 1825, 516–519.
14. Plymley J. *A general view of the agriculture of Shropshire*. London, R. Phillips, 1803.
15. Shropshire County Record Office, 567.
16. *Op. cit.*, ref. 5.
17. Owen and Blakeway, *op. cit.*, 516.
18. *Shrewsbury Chronicle*, 1 May, 1779.

19. *Ibid.*, 13 June, 1780.
20. *Ibid.*, 27 Jan., 1781.
21. See Nichol J. D. Social and political stability in 18th century provincial life: a study of the career of John Ashby of Shrewsbury. *Trans. Shrops. Archaeol. nat. Hist. Soc.*, 1969–70, 54, 53–62.
22. *Shrewsbury Chronicle*, 26 Nov., 1785.
23. Minshull. *Shrewsbury visitor's pocket companion or Salopian guide.* 1786 edition.
24. *Shrewsbury Chronicle*, 9 Sept., 1786.
25. *Ibid.*, 17 Feb., 1787.
26. *Ibid.*, 28 Oct., 1791.
27. Minshull, *op. cit.*, 1803 edition.
28. Owen and Blakeway, *op. cit.*, 518; *Shrewsbury Chronicle*, 14 May, 1802; 9 Nov., 1804.
29. Hulbert C. *History of Shrewsbury*, Vol. 1. 1837, 274; *Shrewsbury Chronicle*, 9 Sept., 1808.
30. Mavor W. *A tour in Wales and through several counties of England performed in the summer of 1805.* 1806, 125.
31. *Shrewsbury Chronicle*, 3 Sept., 1802; 9 Nov., 1804.
32. Mavor, *op. cit.*, 135.
33. *Shrewsbury Chronicle*, 11 Aug., 1 Sept., 6 Oct., 1815.
34. *Ibid.*, 11 Aug., 1815.
35. 2nd Report of Commissioners on Holyhead Roads and Harbour. BPP, 1810.
37. Report on Shrewsbury–Holyhead Road. BPP, 1836, 36.
38. Parnell, Sir H. *A treatise on roads.* 1833, 200–201.
39. *Ibid.*, 209.
40. 1st Report of Select Committee on roads from Holyhead to London. BPP, 1817.
41. *Eddowes Salopian Journal*, 7 Aug., 1816.
42. *Op. cit.* ref. 40; also Report of Committee on Holyhead Roads and Harbour. BPP, 1815.
43. *Ibid*; also 6th Report of Select Committee, Appendix 6. BPP, 1819.
44. 6th Report of Select Committee. BPP, 1819; also 4th Report on Roads from Holyhead to London. BPP, 1822.
45. 1st Report of Commissioners. BPP, 1824.
46. 2nd Report of Commissioners. BPP, 1825.
47. Rickman, *op. cit.*, 228.
48. 3rd Report of Commissioners. BPP, 1827.
49. 4th Report of Commissioners. BPP, 1827.
50. *Op. cit.* ref. 45.
51. 5th Report of Select Committee. BPP, 1817.

52. 4th Report on Roads from Holyhead to London. BPP, 1822.
53. Report of Mr Telford on road from Ketley Ironworks to Chirk. BPP, 1830.
54. Rickman, *op. cit.*, 214.
55. Report of Select Committee. BPP, 1830, 10.
56. *Eddowes Salopian Journal.* 12 April, 19 June, 1815.
57. 5th Report of Commissioners. BPP, 1828, v; also Report of Select Committee. BPP, 1830, 10.
58. Parnell, *op. cit.*, 212; also Report of Select Committee. BPP, 1830, 10.
59. Report of Select Committee. BPP, 1831, 12.
60. 10th Report of Commissioners. BPP, 1833, 17.
61. 18th Report of Commissioners. BPP, 1841, 12.
62. 22nd Report of Commissioners. BPP, 1845, 27; also 23rd Report. BPP, 1846, 24.
63. 3rd Report of Commissioners. BPP, 1826.
64. 23rd Report of Commissioners. BPP, 1846, 24; also 26th Report, 1849, 27.
65. 16th Report of Commissioners. BPP, 1839, 29.
66. *Shrewsbury Chronicle*, 8 Sept., 1837.
67. Trinder B. The memoir of William Smith. *Trans. Shrop. Archaeol. nat. Hist. Soc.*, 1966, 58, 183–184.
68. 28th Report of Commissioners. BPP, 1851, 29.

~ 4 ~

Telford and the design for a
new London Bridge

A. W. SKEMPTON

The exceptionally fine engraving of a proposed 600 ft span bridge in cast iron, designed by Telford to replace old London Bridge, haunts the imagination of all who have seen it, even in reproduction. Reactions vary from an unbounded admiration for the boldness and beauty of the design to disbelief in its practicability. But despite the interest aroused, little information is readily available on the origins of the design, and still less has been published (at any rate since 1817) on the technical aspects.

In an attempt to correct this somewhat remarkable state of affairs I shall first sketch in the history of the scheme, then assess its feasibility in the light both of contemporary and modern knowledge and, after giving what in my opinion are the main reasons why the bridge was not built, conclude with a very brief resumé of subsequent advances in the design of iron arch bridges; a subject in which Telford played a leading role.

History of the project

Throughout the 18th century all but the smallest sea-going vessels using the Port of London moored in the Thames, downstream of London Bridge, and off-loaded into barges or lighters which carried the cargoes to various riverside quays. Though the moorings extended almost continuously along both banks from the bridge to Limehouse and Deptford, the great increase in trade during the second half of the century caused the river to become seriously congested, with resulting difficulties in navigation, heavy losses due to plunder, and excessive delays in handling cargoes.

The most favoured solution to these problems was to consruct large wet docks with warehouses, controlled, where necessary, by customs officers. During the 1790s several other schemes emerged, but all proposals were examined by Parliament and, after intensive investigations, it became clear that the two most viable projects involved docks for general use at Wapping and docks at the Isle of Dogs for the West India trade. Ships up to 500 or 600 tons burden were to be accommodated and the docks would be of sufficient size (indeed, of quite unprecedented size) to reduce very substantially the numbers of ships moored in the river.[1]

However, in March 1798, when these plans were beginning to crystallize, Sir Frederick Morton Eden put forward the idea of replacing old London Bridge by a five-span iron bridge built at a height to allow the passage of 200 ton ships.[2] In this way the river between London and Blackfriars Bridge could be added to the port facilities. Inspired by the successful completion in 1796 of the iron bridge at Sunderland, 100 ft above the River Wear and of 236 ft span, Sir Frederick saw no technical reason why five 150 ft spans at a rather lower height could not be built in London, and he went on to sketch plans for warehouses and two small docks for lighters on the north river bank between the bridges.

In November 1798 Ralph Dodd elaborated the idea with his customary enthusiasm, and drew up a design (exhibited next year at the Royal Academy) for a bridge having a central iron arch of 300 ft span rising 100 ft above high water for the passage of 600 ton vessels.[3] And in 1799 a young Scottish engineer, James Douglass, followed Eden's scheme more closely in a pamphlet proposing an asymmetric five-span iron bridge, the main arch of which spanned 200 ft at a height of 80 ft above high water, admitting ships of 500 tons burden with the top-gallant mast struck.[4]

The approaches to any of these bridges would evidently give rise to problems in London where, unlike Sunderland, the land adjoining the river is low-lying. But the possibility of extending the port to Blackfriars seemed so attractive that a Select Committee was formed at the beginning of May 1799 to consider the whole question. With commendable speed the Committee reported on 1 June that, while nothing should stand in the way of the West India Docks Bill, then nearing the end of its passage, or of a Bill for the London Docks at Wapping in a later session, nevertheless as an adjunct to the docks the bridge scheme would provide welcome additional accommodation for relatively small vessels and should be thoroughly investigated.[5]

Next month, on 12 July, the Act for building the West India Docks was obtained, and under the direction of William Jessop construction began in February 1800. Meanwhile, also in July 1799, the Select Committee issued a second report containing much evidence on the old bridge, on the river, on trade and shipping in the port etc.[6] This report led Parliament in February 1800 to order the examination of further designs for a new London Bridge, and in April the Select Committee called for plans to be submitted; specifically for a bridge with 65 ft headroom above high water suitable for the passage of ships of 200 tons burden. Several engineers responded, and the designs were published by the Committee in their third report dated 28 July 1800, a lengthy document accompanied by 21 large folding engraved plans.[7]

Before considering this report, it should be noted that the Act for London Docks had been passed on 20 June 1800, and that construction, under John Rennie, began about a year later. So work was under way on two dock schemes by mid-1801. Moreover these had entirely adequate financial backing and full approval of the Corporation of London as the statutory port authority.

Turning now to the designs in the third report, pride of place must go to the plans by Thomas Wilson, the engineer of Sunderland Bridge. His elevation (Fig. 1) shows three spans with well proportioned masonry piers and abutments 740 ft apart. The structural ironwork was similar to that used at Sunderland (namely, short open-frame voussoir ribs with circular spandrel frames) and the central span of 240 ft exceeded that of the prototype by only 4 ft. But, as shown in the drawing, the abutments are too slender to take the thrusts from the 220 ft side spans and there is inadequate cross-bracing between the ribs.

Designs for a three-span and also for a five-span iron structure (Fig. 2) were submitted by Telford and Douglass, as well as the asymmetric five-span scheme of 1799. The Committee considered the latter to be so disagreeable in appearance that the drawing was not engraved, but four other drawings (Pls IX–XII of the report) were reproduced. These include a map, a general elevation, and two detailed elevations drawn by William Jones. The north and south approach ramps, following the bridge axis, are shown with a gradient of about 1:10. Ramps along the wharfs were also proposed and these had a gradient of 1:16; figures to be compared with Hol-

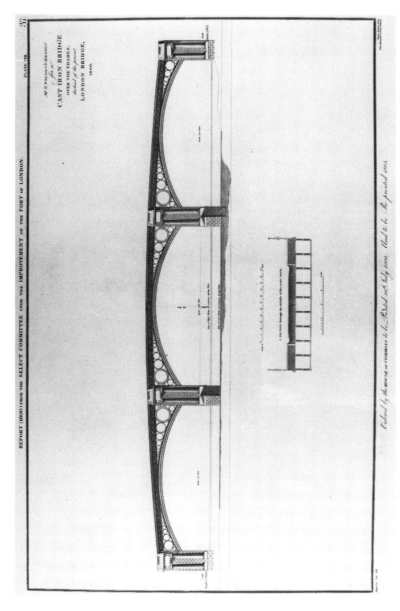

Fig. 1. Wilson's design for new London Bridge

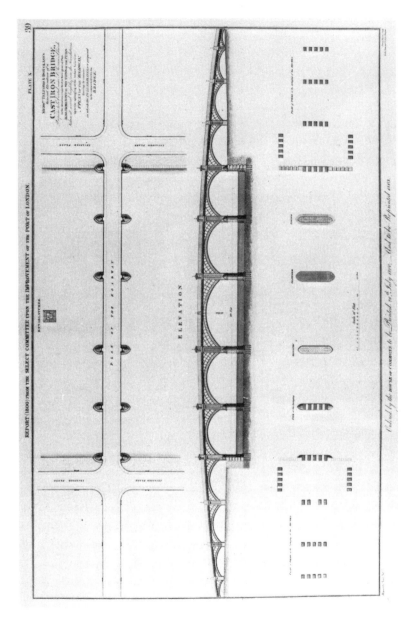

Fig. 2. Five-span design by Telford and Douglass

born Hill which, at 1:17, was reckoned as inconveniently steep for horse-drawn waggons. So the approaches would have had to be lengthened in practice to produce acceptable slopes.

Telford is not mentioned in the 1799 pamphlet, but he and Douglass were well acquainted at that time and there is evidence that he had already become involved in the bridge scheme.[8] Certainly he carried the responsibility in 1800 and 1801 for all structural aspects of the designs, as Douglass, though a clever and ambitious engineer (with three patents to his name by 1799), had no experience and probably very little knowledge of bridges. In 1802 he suddenly left London and went on to a successful career in France, apparently in the textile business.[9]

In the third report, then, there are drawings for three iron bridges, two by Telford and Douglass, and one by Wilson. In addition, Samuel Wyatt sent in a model of a fourth, but he had no time to prepare plans and estimates. Ralph Dodd submitted a new design in July 1800, this time for a monumental masonry bridge with four-storey warehouses along the north and south quays carried above ground level on cast-iron columns. Robert Mylne, the engineer of Blackfriars Bridge, reported at length on the river and existing bridges, and also discussed generally a proposal for a five-arch masonry bridge with attention to the architectural and planning problems involved. These were formidable, and George Dance, Surveyor to the City, proposd to overcome them by a radically different scheme for a low-level bridge having a central lifting span to allow the passage of ships. Associated with his proposal, which may be thought of as containing the germ of an idea expressed a century later in Tower Bridge, he drew up beautiful designs for piazzas at each end of the bridge and for warehouses. Finally, at the request of the City, Jessop reported on the effects of building new embankments between London and Blackfriars Bridge and concluded that the regime of the river when deepened by dredging might even be improved by narrowing its width to 600 ft.

In conclusion, the Committee recommended that London Bridge should be replaced by an iron bridge, 65 ft above high water, and that the river should be embanked, with warehouses on the embankments. Probably as the Session was drawing to a close, Parliament merely ordered that the report be 'laid on the Table' and printed.

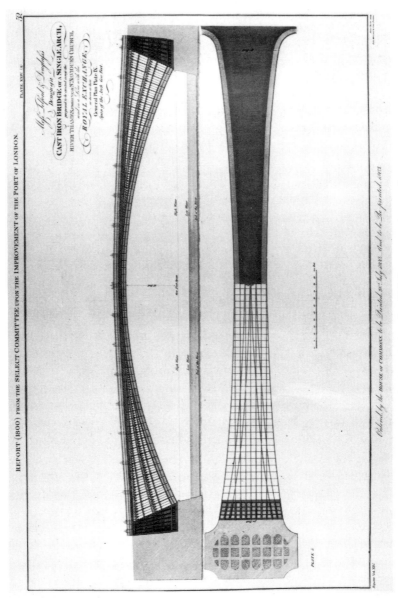

Fig. 3. First design for 600 ft span cast iron arch

However, in the autumn of 1800 and too late to be included in the third report, Telford and Douglass, seizing on the 600 ft width suggested by Jessop, submitted a revolutionary scheme for bridging the river by a single cast-iron arch of 600 ft span. A plan and elevation (Fig. 3) engraved by Wilson Lowry as Pl. XXIV, a brief report and estimates, and a three-span masonry bridge design by James Black, were issued by the Committee as a Supplemental Appendix.[10] An architectural model of the 600 ft span bridge was also made and installed in the Royal Academy by the end of December 1800.

The design naturally aroused great interest and the Select Committee took urgent steps to ascertain its practicability.

'The obvious Advantages' they wrote, 'which would be obtained if the Communication could be effected by means of a Single Arch, as well as the Magnificence of the proposed Structure, appeared to give the Design a particular Claim to the notice of your Committee; yet the Attempt was of so novel a Nature, that they thought it absolutely necessary for their own Information as well as for the Purpose of affording some Grounds upon which the House might hereafter form their Judgment as to its Expediency, to request the opinions of some of the Persons most eminent in Great Britain for their Theoretic as well as Practical Knowledge of such Subjects.[11]

As a result of this decision, Telford began in January 1801 making a list of questions (he wrote four drafts),[12] and after preliminary correspondence with several of the 'experts' he produced additional drawings (Fig. 4) of two possible methods of cross-framing the ribs, and of an alternative design for the ribs and spandrel framing.[13] The latter is noteworthy as containing the first hints of the structural style later to be embodied by Telford in his series of iron arch bridges starting with Bonar in 1811.

The questions, together with the new drawings, were sent out early in April 1801, and the replies (as letters to Telford and as 'official' answers to the Committee) nearly all date from the last two weeks of that month. The letters are among Telford's papers at the Institution of Civil Engineers, and the Select Committee published the questions and answers, with an engraving of the new drawings, in their fourth (and final) report issued on 3 June, 1801.[11] The report also includes a sketch design by John Southern for another 600 ft span iron bridge and a variant by Samuel Bentham of Dance's low-level scheme.

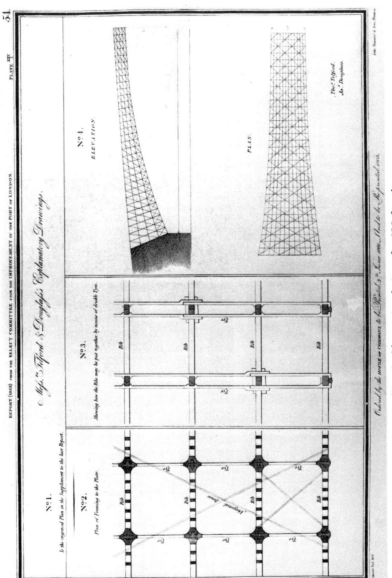

Fig. 4. Alternative designs for 600 ft arch

Those taking part in the enquiry included the Astronomer Royal, Nevil Maskelyne; the academics Abraham Robertson of Oxford, George Atwood of London (formerly of Trinity College, Cambridge), John Robison and John Playfair, professors respectively of Natural Philosophy and Mathematics at Edinburgh, and Charles Hutton of the Royal Military Academy at Woolwich; the engineers William Jessop, John Rennie, James Watt, and John Southern (Watt's assistant); Charles Bage of Shrewsbury; and the ironmasters John Wilkinson and William Reynolds. The number and distinction of these men provide eloquent proof of the importance attached to the investigation, and it may be added that Thomas Young contributed his own detailed answers to the questions in an article published in 1817.[14]

A full analysis of the answers and the letters, which give a conspectus of contemporary knowledge on iron arch bridges, would require a separate study. Here one must be content with a brief mention of some of the salient points, dealt with later. But the general conclusion is clear: too little was known, and the differences of opinion among the answers were too great for the Committee to make any definite recommendations. Indeed their fourth report contains no proposals of any kind and, when submitted to the House of Commons, it was simply ordered to lie on the table and be printed.

Though no further official action followed, the printing of the fourth report is not the end of the story. Encouraged by Hutton, Telford wrote an article on the 600 ft span proposal which was published in June 1801 in the *Philosophical Magazine* and reprinted with slight variations in July in the *Monthly Magazine*.[15] He also set about issuing the superb aquatint engraving (Fig. 5) first published by Ackermann in October 1801 and later, with a dedication to George III, in 1802.[16]

In this work of art, for such it is, the bridge was engraved by Wilson Lowry and the general view by Thomas Malton. Subscribers received an accompanying pamphlet, essentially a reissue of the article previously mentioned, and a second edition was published in 1802.[17] Printings of the engraving continued for at least 16 years.[18] Along with many other parliamentary reports, all four of the Select Committee reports and the Supplemental Appendix were reprinted in 1803,[19] with many of the plates being

Fig. 5. Aquatint engraving of proposed 600 ft span bridge

engraved anew by James Basire on a smaller and more convenient
scale. These have been used for the illustrations to this paper.

Young, as we have seen, examined the technical aspects of the
design again in 1817, and Cresy published a lengthy summary of
the 1801 report in his *Encyclopaedia of civil engineering* in 1847.
Small-scale engravings appeared in several articles during the first
half of the 19th century, and the famous aquatint has been reproduced frequently in modern books on Telford and on the history of
bridges.

Analysis of the design

Erection. It may be supposed that the abutments would first be
built up to springing level. Erection of the arch ribs would then
follow, the ribs being carried on timber centering supported on
trestle frames rising from the river bed on piled foundations, as
shown in the well-known engraving by J. Raffield after Robert
Clarke, of Sunderland Bridge under construction. Finally the abutments and superstructure would be completed, and the
approaches. Handling the voussoirs might have been difficult, as
each would have weighed about 8 tons, but the really daunting
problem was that of obtaining an accurate bearing between the
radial faces of the voussoir frames, and in practice Telford would
probably have modified the design so that only the upper and lower
arcs were in contact, not the entire face. Robison suggested this

modification, following the Sunderland design. Even so, the 'facing up' of two surfaces, totalling 200 sq. in. in area, at each of 832 joints, can only be regarded as a task likely to cause grave misgivings in the mind of any prospective ironwork contractor.

Approaches. Deck level at each end of the bridge was about 60 ft above ground. In the 1801 engraving the E–W approaches are in the form of arcaded ramps, not iron arches as in 1800. The gradients are not given, nor are the intended form or gradient of the main N–S approaches, but assuming 1:20 as a maximum possible figure (Rennie's London Bridge of 1831 with a headroom of 28 ft above high water had approach gradients of 1:24), the ramps would have extended nearly 400 yds beyond the abutment, i.e. well past Cannon Street on the north side. It was to avoid such problems that Dance proposed a low-level, draw-bridge scheme.

Headroom for shipping. The 600 ft span had a rise of 65 ft, with the crown of the arch 68 ft above high water. This was ample for 200 ton ships in mid-stream but, unlike a three-span bridge, the single-span design provided only restricted headroom near the abutments. Several of the commentators pointed to this defect.

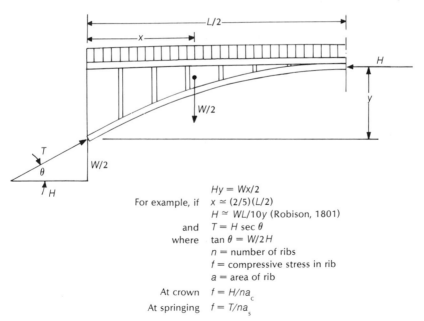

$$Hy = Wx/2$$

For example, if $x \simeq (2/5)(L/2)$
$H \simeq WL/10y$ (Robison, 1801)

and $T = H \sec \theta$

where $\tan \theta = W/2H$
n = number of ribs
f = compressive stress in rib
a = area of rib

At crown $f = H/na_c$

At springing $f = T/na_s$

Fig. 6. Approximate theory for rib stress calculation

Arch thrust. Robison, Playfair, Hutton and Atwood all present valid methods of calculating the arch thrust. Robison's is explained in Fig. 6 and his figure of 9320 tons for the horizontal thrust (or 10 500 tons for the inclined thrust at the abutments) compares closely with the result given later by Young.[14]

Robison made a reasonable assumption for the weight of road-way (equivalent to 220 lb/sq. ft) but some of the commentators forget this important part of the load, which amounts to about 3600 tons,* and use only the weight of iron: estimated at 6500 tons. It seems to have been customary at the time to take no account of live loading on arch bridges; but allowing 40 lb/sq. ft I find the abutment thrust to be approximately 12 000 tons acting at an inclination of 25½° to the horizontal. This angle is only 1° steeper than the inclination of the ribs at the springing.

For calculations of abutment stability and settlement a smaller live load can be used for an average long-term condition, and I have taken the corresponding thrust as 11 000 tons.

Spandrel framing. In formulating the questions, Telford was concerned with the possibility that the whole of the ironwork could act together as a single frame. Maskelyne took this idea to an absurd extreme, judging that the bridge might act as a girder applying no thrust to the abutments. But Jessop, Southern, Bage and others emphasised that only the two lower continuous arcs can take the thrust, acting as an arch. The sole structural function of the framing above was to transfer the deck load to the arch ribs. James Watt particularly disapproved of the higher 'ribs' and said the spandrel frames should be vertical. Telford's second sketch (Fig. 4) shows how clearly he had grasped these general principles by April 1801. It is also notable for the first introduction of diagonal cross bracing.

Rib stress. For an accurate calculation of the *maximum* rib stress it is necessary to know the magnitude and line of action of the thrust at all points in the arch, and the cross-sectional area of the rib elements or arcs. The effects of variations in temperature should also be taken into account. Such calculations were not made in 1801; nor

---

* Robison's figure. In a letter to Atwood, dated 21 Jan 1801 (Nat. Lib. Scotland MS 2909, f16), Telford gives a roadway weight corresponding to 300 lb/sq. ft. This is unusually high and would result in an abutment thrust of about 13 000 tons or 5 ton/sq. in. rib stress.

will they be attempted here, as I think it is sufficient to estimate the *average* rib stress at springing (where the thrust is greatest) and compare the result with equivalent figures for iron arch bridges actually built in the early 19th century.

Before doing so, however, reference must be made to possible eccentricity of the line of thrust. Telford seems to have appreciated this factor, as in his second design (Fig. 4) he increases the depth of the arch rib to about 13 ft at the springing, in contrast to a uniform depth of about 9 ft in the first plan. Several of the commentators consider the problem of the thrust line, though I must confess some difficulty in following their arguments, but Thomas Young clearly indicates that the thrust could be substantially above mid-height of the arch at distances around 50–100 ft from the springing. If correct, this implies much greater loads in the upper than in the lower arcs of the ribs, and justifies the use of a large factor of safety in terms of average stresses.

No detailed drawings of the ribs were provided, but by scaling off the elevation and framing plan the cross-sectional area of each rib is found to be approximately 200 sq. in. (i.e. 100 sq. in. for each of the arcs). In the first design there are seven parallel ribs, two slightly curved ribs, and four long oblique ribs. Just how the total thrust would be distributed between these is uncertain. But in the second scheme (Fig. 4) a much improved system of thirteen independent ribs is shown. In this later arrangement, then, the average compression stress in the ribs at springing level is $12\,000/(13 \times 200)$ = 4½ tons/sq. in. And, for reasons just given, the maximum rib stress might be appreciably higher.

None of the commentators made this simple calculation, and indeed a not unusual view seems to have been that cast iron is so strong in compression as scarcely to make the rib stress a limiting factor in design. Such a conclusion apparently received support from pioneer tests carried out by William Reynolds in April 1801, from which he found the compression strength of a small cube of cast iron to be 64 tons/sq. in.[20]

This result is correct, but it is irrelevant to the problem, as Reynolds himself must have known. For in 1795, probably in connection with designing the supports of Longdon Aqueduct, tests had been made at Ketley to determine the breaking load of cast-iron struts 1 in. square in section and 36 in. long; and they failed at 5 tons/sq. in. Moreover, in the cruciform section supports of the aqueduct the compression stress does not exceed 1 ton/sq. in.

Surprisingly, Reynolds in his replies to the Committee, and to Telford, makes no reference to the Ketley tests, but Bage gives details of them in a note to Telford, and elsewhere points out that the ribs in the bridge will act as 'pillars',[21] by which he means the slender iron columns already used by himself in the flax mill at Shrewsbury (1796–97) and by William Strutt in mills at Derby (1792–93) and Belper (1793–95).[22] These columns had been carefully proportioned in relation to the loads (up to 40 tons) they had to carry, with a compressive stress around 2½ tons/sq. in. (the exact figure depending a little on the assumed live loading on the floors), and in another letter to Telford, written on 12 April, 1801, Bage says that the ribs of the bridge will readily bear a load corresponding to 2 tons/sq. in.

In fact, if it is correct to assume that each main element in the ribs was about 8 × 12 in. (making an area of 100 sq. in.) then the ribs, being about 10 ft long between the cross-bracing, were less slender than the mill columns; and a safe stress would have been about 3 tons/sq. in. This is approximately the rib stress in Wilson's bridges at Sunderland and Staines, though calculations which I have made for these and other large iron-arch bridges show (Fig. 7) that the general practice after 1801 was to keep the stresses very much the same as Bage's 2 tons/sq. in.

In his reply to the Committee, Bage makes the point about the ribs acting as pillars, but is too modest to say that as early as 1796 he had worked out a theory for the strength of cast iron columns, of rectangular or cruciform cross section.[22] Here, without going into details, I shall merely note that in practice it compares well with the later widely accepted method of Rankine and Gordon. John Southern made the same point, and recommended that tests be carried out to determine the strength of iron struts 1 in. square by 12 in. long. This sensible suggestion was taken still further by Wilkinson, who advised testing a large-scale model of the arch and even a full-scale test on a rib element, and offered to carry out such tests himself. However, he preferred the three-span design. Reynolds also advised the use of a model, as did Rennie.

Thus, in conclusion, a stress around 4½ tons/sq. in. must be regarded as exceptionally high, though probably not dangerous.

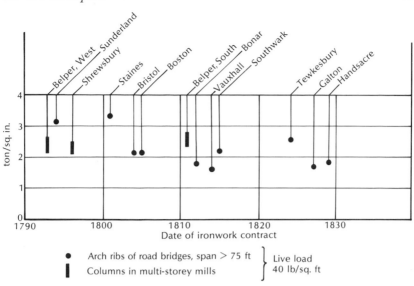

Fig. 7. Compression stresses in cast iron structures

But in 1801 the confusion and lack of knowledge on this aspect of the design was a serious matter.

Abutments. It is evident that the abutments had been designed with care. As shown in Fig. 3 they are broadened out to a width of 130 ft, giving a base area of 13 200 sq. ft, and the centre of gravity was thrown forward by leaving cavities in the back part of the structure. Admittedly, in Fig. 3 the cavities are shown filled with rubble, but in a sketch made in January 1801 Telford indicates somewhat larger cavities and without filling.[23] In their estimates Telford and Douglas quote volumes of granite and brickwork as if for both abutments,[10] but it is clear that these actually apply to one abutment only; and the weight (assuming no filling) amounts to 63 000 tons. The resultant force of this weight and the arch thrust, with an allowance for the relatively small earth pressure acting on the back face, lies well inside the middle third of the base and gives a nominal pressure distribution as shown in Fig. 8. Had the abutments been founded on rock, there could be no question of their stability. But in fact they rested on alluvial gravel a few feet above a thick bed of London Clay.

Rennie thought the clay to be of sufficient strength for the construction of an abutment to resist the arch thrust, but probably, like

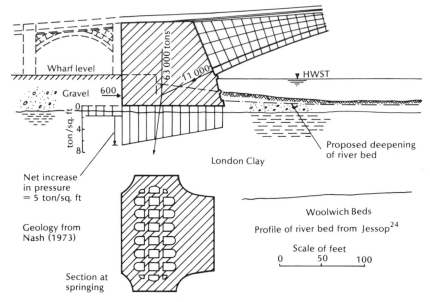

Fig. 8. Sections of proposed north abutment of bridge

Southern, he would have liked to use raking piles. Watt wanted
deep exploratory excavations at both sites and borings from the
bottom of these pits to ascertain the ground conditions, while
Robison anticipated trouble from long-term yielding of the abutments and pointed out that for every inch of horizontal movement
at the springing, the crown would sink by 5 in.

Here we have the greatest uncertainty in the whole design. I am
not saying that adequate abutments could not have been built, even
in 1801, but they would have had to be deeper, and preferably on
piled foundations, and it is questionable whether with the knowledge then available any design could have been proved to be safe
before construction started.

To arrive at approximate quantitative estimates of the behaviour
of the abutments as designed, I have taken data on the London Clay
from recent investigations for the new London Bridge, and the settlement records of Rennie's bridge during construction and over
the 140 years of its existence.[25] The calculations are not given here,
for lack of space (some of them are tediously long in any case), but
the results are summarized in Table 1. Briefly, they show an
uncomfortably low factor of safety against sliding, and a lower

than usual factor of safety against a foundation failure in the clay. The mean settlements, though large, are not in themselves disturbing but of course the non-uniform pressures produce a tilt, and this translates into a horizontal component of movement at springing level of the order of 2 in., i.e. a spread of the arch of 4 in. And this must be a minimum figure, as there would also be some movement due to shear deformations which I have not calculated.

Now Wilson's iron arch bridge at Staines, opened in 1803, suffered severe damage and had to be taken down, as the result of a 3 in. horizontal movement of one abutment.[26] Its span was 181 ft. Once again, then, we find a very uncomfortable feature in the design; especially when it is remembered that the rib stresses would have been exceptionally high even without yielding abutments.

Reasons for not building the bridge

The most important reason, in my opinion, why the bridge was not built arose from the unprecedented scale of the project, coupled with lack of knowledge of and agreement on the technical factors involved. In this respect there is a vital difference between the 600 ft span London Bridge proposal, on the one hand, and, on the other, Telford's Menai suspension bridge and Stephenson's Britannia box girder bridge. In the two latter designs, calculations and tests could

Table 1. Approximate stability and settlement calculations for abutment; construction period taken as 3 years, weight of abutment 63 000 tons, arch thrust 11 000 tons

	End of construction	After 50 years	Final values
Factor of safety against sliding	1.7	2.5	2.5
Factor of safety, bearing capacity	1.7	2.0	2.0
Mean settlement	6 in.	9 in.	10½ in.
Tilt	0.2°	0.25°	0.3°
Horizontal movement of springing (minimum calculated values)	1½ in.	2 in.	2½ in.

be, and were, carried out and the work went ahead with reasonable confidence despite the unprecedented nature of the bridges in scale and (for Britannia Bridge) the structural system.

A second factor is that the approaches presented serious planning problems. There is additionally no evidence that the Corporation of London, the authority principally involved, looked with any favour on a high-level bridge; the City Surveyor in fact produced an alternative low-level scheme.

By August 1802 the first of the great West India Docks was opened to shipping. London Docks at Wapping followed in January 1805, the second West India Dock in July 1806, and the East India Docks at Blackwall a month later (the East India Company having obtained their Dock Act in 1803). The docks fulfilled the promise foreseen in the 1790s and the need for extending the port activities upstream of London Bridge faded away.

Finally the economic climate was unfavourable for publicly financed non-strategic projects at a time of war.

Subsequent developments

The period around 1800 was one of ebullient confidence in the possibilities of structural cast iron. Buildwas and Sunderland bridges and Longdon Aqueduct had recently been completed. Rennie proposed a 450 ft span for an iron arch bridge over the Menai Straits in 1802, and in the same year work began on the iron arches and trough of Pontcysyllte; completed with triumphant success in 1805.

But in 1804–06 Staines Bridge proved to be a complete failure owing to abutment movements. Sunderland Bridge by 1805 was in a perilous condition, having warped nearly 2 ft out of line due to the absence of adequate cross-bracing. It was rescued by John Grimshaw's remedial measures in that year. In 1806 the Coalbrookdale Company had a bridge collapse during construction at Bristol, and Walkers of Rotherham had a similar disaster at Yarm; and in 1807 Rennie and Wilson were experiencing trouble with their bridge at Boston.

However, a ray of hope gleamed through this now very gloomy scene. Though one of the two identical bridges at Bristol designed by Jessop collapsed, this was due to a fault in erection (acknowledged by the Dale Company) and both bridges were successfully opened to traffic in 1807 in accordance with the original design. This embodied, as a novel feature, ribs made of long iron plates perforated to lighten their weight and rigidly bolted together through flanges at their ends. Nothing of note happened during the next three years until, in 1810, Thomas Wilson and Henry Provis (father of Telford's assistant W. A. Provis) built the 60 ft span bridge at Newport Pagnell on the Sunderland-Staines principles with some significant improvements. It remains today in excellent condition, the oldest iron bridge still carrying trunk road traffic.

But the real break-through occurred in 1811–12 with the construction of the 150 ft span Bonar Bridge, designed by Telford with ironwork by William Hazledine of Pontcysyllte fame. This incorporated perforated plate ribs developed from the Bristol bridges, improved lateral bracing, and radial lozenge-frame spandrels. Except for a single change to the more logical vertical lozenge spandrels, as seen in the finest of all cast-iron bridges at Tewkesbury (170 ft span, built 1824–26, again with ironwork by Hazledine), Telford used the Bonar system throughout the rest of his very distinguished career as a bridge builder in cast iron.

Bonar Bridge restored confidence. Telford himself immediately repeated the design at Craigellachie (1813–14). James Walker unhesitatingly used iron for Vauxhall Bridge (1813–16), introducing I-section ribs, and with Southwark Bridge (1814–19) Rennie achieved the largest span, of 240 ft, ever built in cast iron.[27]

Acknowledgements

I am grateful to Mr J. G. James and Mr Roland Paxton for information and helpful discussions on iron arch bridges in general and the 600 ft span design in particular. Mr Alan Butcher found the very rare Supplemental Appendix, in the Goodrich Collection at the Science Museum, and Miss Julia Elton of Weinreb Ltd showed me the equally rare accompanying plates. The aquatint is reproduced by kind permission of Mr E. Thomas, General Manager of Telford Development Corporation, from a photograph made at my request by the Ironbridge Gorge Museum Trust.

References
1. Skempton A. W. Engineering in the Port of London, 1789–1808. *Trans. Newcomen Soc.*, 1979, 50.

2. Eden, Sir F. M. *Porto-Bello; or, a plan for the improvement of the Port and City of London.* London, 1798.

3. Dodd R. *Letters to a merchant, on the improvement of the Port of London.* London, 1798.

4. *Explanation of a plan, for improving the Port of London,* 1799.

5. Report from the Select Committee appointed to consider evidence taken on Bills for the improvement of the Port of London. 1 June, 1799.

6. Second Report from the Select Committee upon the improvement of the Port of London. 11 July, 1799.

7. Third Report from the Select Committee . . . , 28 July, 1800, issued with a separate large double-folio volume 'The several plans and drawings referred to in the Third Report . . .'.

8. Telford to Little, 13 May, 1800. Gibb, Sir A. *The story of Telford.* London, Alexander Machose, 1935.

9. *Ex. inf.* Mr J. G. James. See also Gibb, *op. cit.*

10. Supplement to Third Report (Supplemental Appendix), issued in the second half of 1800 with three separate large folding engraved plates. Plate 24 (64 × 182 cm) is entitled 'Messrs Telford & Douglass's Design of a Cast Iron Bridge of a Single Arch proposed to be erected across the River Thames . . . Span of the Arch 600 Feet'.

11. Fourth Report from the Select Committee . . . 3 June, 1801. Issued with three folding engraved plates.

12. Telford Mss, Institution of Civil Engineers.

13. Originals of these three drawings, signed by Telford, are among the Telford Mss in the ICE. They appear as plate 1, engraved by J. Barlow in the Fourth Report, under the names of Telford and Douglass.

14. Young T. Bridges. *Encyclopaedia Britannica, Supplement.* 1817. Vol. 2, 507–516.

15. An account of the improvements of the port of London, and more particularly of the intended bridge, consisting of a single arch of 600 feet. *Phil. Mag.*, 1801, 10, 59–67; also *Monthly Mag.*, 1801, 11, 477–481.

16. *Perspective view of the design for a cast iron bridge, consisting of a single arch 600 feet in the span, and calculated to supply the place of the present London Bridge.* Hand-coloured aquatint engraving, 65 × 125 cm. In its first state, published October 1801, the plate is inscribed 'To the Right Honourable Lord Hawksbury . . . Chairman of the Select Committee for Improving the Port of London . . . by his obedient Servants, Thomas Telford & James Douglass'. In a letter to Andrew Little of 14 April, 1802, Telford writes that the plate is 'in future to be dedicated to the King', and the second issue is inscribed 'To George

the Third, King of the United Kingdom ... by his most faithfull Subject, Thomas Telford'.

17. *An account of the improvements of the Port of London, and more particularly of the intended iron bridge, consisting of one arch of six hundred feet span.* London, 1801. Reprinted with new title page, 1802.

18. I have been informed of a print in a private collection on paper water-marked 1818.

19. *Reports from Committees of the House of Commons*, vol. 14, 1803.

20. William Reynolds to Telford, 23 April, 1801. Telford Mss, ICE.

21. Charles Bage to Telford, 23 April, 1801. Telford Mss, ICE. Bage's (undated) note on the Ketley tests may have been an enclosure in this letter. The tests are recorded in Telford's Memorandum Book, printed in Rickman, *Life of Thomas Telford*. London, 1838, 682.

22. Skempton A. W. and Johnson H. R. The first iron frames. *Architect. Rev.*, 1962, 131, 175–186.

23. Telford's first draft of the questionnaire. Telford Mss, ICE.

24. Jessop W. *In* Third Report from the Select Committee. July, 1800.

25. Nash J. K. T. L. In discussion on Brown, London Bridge: planning, design and supervision. *Proc. Instn Civ. Engrs*, 1973, 54, 726–732.

26. James J. G. Thomas Wilson's cast-iron bridges 1800–1810. *Trans. Newcomen Soc.*, (to be published).

27. Details of the bridges mentioned in this section of the paper can be found in Paxton R. *The influence of Thomas Telford on the use of improved constructional materials in civil engineering practice.* MSc thesis, Heriot-Watt University, 1975.

~ 5 ~

Menai Bridge 1818–26

Evolution of design*

ROLAND A. PAXTON

The first significant period of iron suspension bridge building in modern times occurred in North America about 1800. This development stimulated interest in Britain, and an era began which led to the establishment of the suspension bridge as the means of achieving the largest spans. This period, dominated by Menai Bridge, effectively began in 1811 and was one of substantially progressive development for about two decades, followed by a time of consolidation and occasional improvements. The art spread to France about 1823 onwards with the subsequent emphasis, particularly after 1830, on suspension from wire cables. At the approach to the middle of the century the mainstream of development returned to the USA.

The experimentally based design practice of an American judge, James Finley,[1] exemplified in the Merrimack Bridge, Massachusetts, of 244 ft span and built in 1810, had little influence on British practice, although his bridges, in demonstrating the practicability of the wrought iron suspension bridge concept, gave impetus generally to the development of this type of structure. The attitude of contemporary British engineers to Finley's work is reflected in Telford's comment that 'British dexterity upon superior materials' would improve on the North American bridges.[2]

The origins of the evolution of the Menai Bridge design can be traced to a Telford proposal of 1811 for a cast-iron bridge to carry the London to Holyhead Road over the Menai Strait, close to the site eventually adopted for the suspension bridge. A 500 ft span cast-iron arch was proposed, and because of the impracticability of

*This paper is a shortened and revised version of that published in *Trans. Newcomen Soc.*, 1979, 49, 27–110, and is reprinted by permission of the Society.

providing adequate support for the arch centering from the bottom of the deep and rocky tideway in fast moving water, Telford proposed suspending the centering from above (Fig. 1). The centering was to have consisted of four parallel rib frames spanning the waterway in sections and supported by a series of 1½ in. square section iron stays, radiating two to a frame from timber side towers of quadrant elevation. Each stay was continuous (presumably welded) from the rib frame to about 50 ft from the tower, where it was attached by a flexible chain to a winch.[3]

Telford's proposed use of continuous iron bar suspension members in preference to link chains, which would have had to be heavier to provide the same strength, demonstrates an efficient approach and furnishes one of the earliest examples of what is now modern practice in respect of the use of steel wire cables. In his calculations Telford assumed the breaking stress of a bar to be 80 000 lb/sq. in. (35.7 tons/sq. in.) and multiplied this figure by the cross-sectional area of the bar to give a 'suspending power' of 180 000 lb.[4] He did not use the term 'stress', which came into general use later, but in applying a proportionality factor it is evident that he understood the concept of the term. The design was optimistic in terms of strength, reflecting the general inadequacy of 'strength of materials' knowledge at that time. Nevertheless, there is little doubt that this ingenious concept, which is typical of Telford's bold and imaginative approach to civil engineering design, could then have been successfully put into effect if the political decision to proceed with the project had been taken. In its use of wrought-iron bars in direct tension as a principal means of support, this proposal can be considered the precursor of the ambitious proposal Telford put forward for a suspension bridge at Runcorn.

Runcorn Bridge project, 1814–18

The experimentally based design work undertaken by Telford in connection with the Runcorn Bridge scheme undoubtedly was the next stage in the evolution of the Menai Bridge design. Although never implemented, this project exercised an important influence on the general development of suspension bridges. The bridge, which was to have crossed the River Mersey at Runcorn Gap, was part of a plan to improve road communication between Liverpool, the Midlands and London. Telford, who became engineer for the

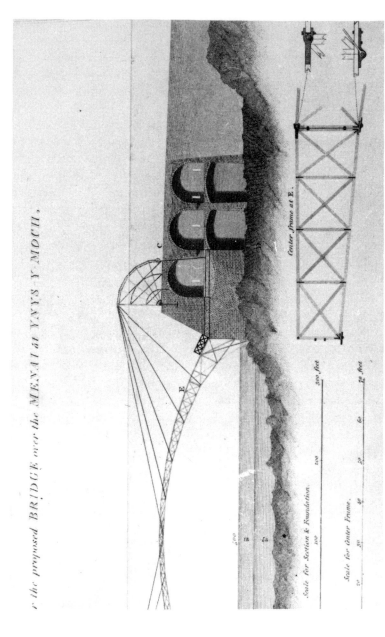

Fig. 1. Menai Bridge cast iron arch proposal 1811: suspended centering design (From Report from Commissioners; ref. 3, plate II)

project in 1814, considered a suspension bridge to be the only practicable way of achieving the crossing, for navigational and foundation reasons, and proposed a structure 2000 ft long with a central clear span of 1000 ft.

A wrought-iron suspension bridge of this magnitude was then quite unprecedented in terms of design, construction and technology, and it was necessary for its projectors to demonstrate its practicability. To provide a basis for his design, Telford made in the spring and summer of 1814 and mainly at Brunton's London cable manufactory:

> '. . . above 200 Experiments upon malleable iron, of from one twentieth to one and a half inch diameter, and on lengths varying from 31 to 900 feet. The Experiments were made perpendicularly, horizontally, and with different degrees of curvature. The Results were that a Bar of good malleable Charcoal Iron, one Inch square, will suspend 27 tons, and that an Iron Wire one tenth of an inch diameter (100 feet of which weighs 3 lb 3 oz) will suspend 700 lbs, and that the latter with a Curvature or versed sine of one fiftieth of the Chord line, will besides its own weight suspend one tenth part of the weight suspended perpendicularly when disposed at one fourth, one half, and three fourths of its length; and that with a Curvature of one twentieth of the Chord line it will suspend one third of the aforesaid perpendicular weight, when disposed in a similar manner. Experiments upon other diameters correspond sufficiently . . .'[5]

In some of these experiments the forces measured were first that at which the permanent elongation of wrought-iron bars began, and then that at which breaking occurred: in modern terms the determination of 'elastic limit' and 'ultimate tensile strength'. From these experiments, which in respect of elastic limit were among the earliest to be conducted, Telford was led to believe that stretching occurred at about 18 tons/sq. in. Later technology would suggest 12–15 tons/sq.in. as a more likely figure. However, he adopted 15 tons/sq. in. and 27 tons/sq. in. for the stretching and breaking limits of wrought-iron bars[6,7] and just under 40 tons/sq. in. for the breaking limit of 0.1 in. dia. iron wire.[8]

Using these strength data Telford made out two sets of calculations and estimates for the bridge, one based on the use of wire cables and the other on the use of bar cables. The principal dimensions of the bridge were the same for both arrangements, namely a central span of 1000 ft, side spans of 500 ft and two pyramidal towers about 140 ft above high water level. The main support was to have been from sixteen cables in four rows, each with a curvature depth from their chord line at mid-span of 1/20th of the span. The roadways were to have derived additional support from a further 26 cables (eight underneath, fourteen at the sides and four diagonal) with a curvature depth of 1/50th of the span, thus introducing a 1 in 12½ maximum longitudinal gradient in the deck adjoining the towers. This arrangement would have provided a headroom of nearly 80 ft above the deepest navigable channel, which was close to the south pier (Fig. 2).

Wire cable design, 1814. The proposal to use cables consisting of many hundreds of small diameter near-parallel wires totalling nearly 13 000 miles in length (Table 1) represents a remarkable design innovation and one that is conceptually close to modern practice. It was supported by the construction and testing under load of a scale model 50 ft in length. Nearly a decade was to pass before Messrs Seguin of Annonay introduced wire suspension bridges on the Continent.

The method of calculating the 'power of suspension' of 2443 tons for this design is illustrated in Table 1. The weight to be suspended, exclusive of that of the cables themselves, as in the experiments, was calculated at 1200 tons, and the safety margin was therefore 1243 tons, which represents a much lower safety factor than that eventually adopted for Menai Bridge. This design can be assumed to have been prepared under Telford's direction by William A. Provis, who first worked for him in 1805 and from 1808 as his pupil, later becoming Resident Engineer for Menai Bridge. The design was not adopted, probably more on grounds of cost rather than because of any doubts about its technical feasibility. Even allowing for the greater strength of the wire cables, the estimates indicate that they would have cost about 60% more than the bar cables.

Bar cable design, 1814. In the alternative bar cable design, each cable in the upper curve was to have consisted of 36½ in. square bars, butt-welded to form continuous elements and making a 3 in. square, with an iron segment on each face to enable the bars to be pressed firmly together (Fig. 3). Waterproofing was to be achieved by filling interstices with a mixture of beeswax and resin, covering

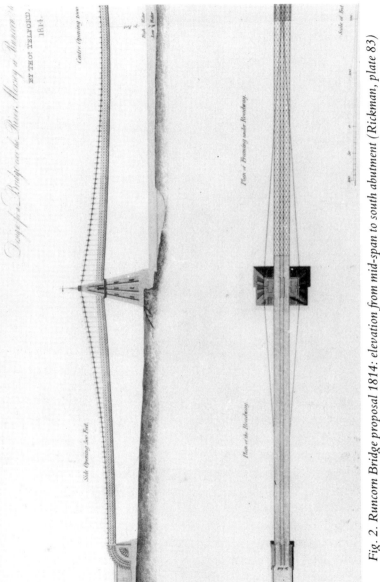

Fig. 2. Runcorn Bridge proposal 1814: elevation from mid-span to south abutment (Rickman, plate 83)

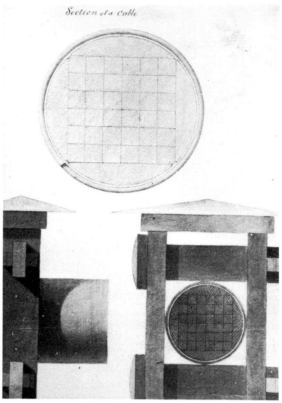

Fig. 3. Runcorn Bridge project 1814–18: proposed composite bar cable detail (Telford drawings, Institution of Civil Engineers)

the surface of the cable with flannel saturated with this compound, and wrapping the whole round with wire. Bucklings were to be provided at 5 ft intervals. A specimen length of cable was made up, in association with Bryan Donkin, an engineer who supported its practicability.

Telford envisaged, as he did for the wire design, that the stresses in the bridge would be equalized between the upper and lower cables. He used the same strength factors as for the wire design but applied to a breaking stress of 27 tons/sq. in. The suspended weight and 'power of suspension' were almost identical with the figures for the wire cable design (Table 1). The maximum stress in the cables on the basis of Telford's experiments would have been about 15.7 tons/sq. in. (15.3 tons/sq. in. from theory) of which nearly 5

Table 1. *Runcorn Bridge project, main details of wire cables and their 'power of suspension' as calculated by Telford for 1000 ft span*

Position in bridge	Cables				Details of 0.1 in. dia. wires 2010 ft long		
	No and dia., in.	No. cable	Wt wire, lb	Total weight tons	Depth mid span, ft	Ultimate load wire, in★	Power of suspension tons
Below roadway	8 × 3.1	754	65	175.0	20	60 (600 × 0.1)	
Intermediate	6 × 2½	500	65	87.1	20	60	349
15 ft above roadway	8 × 2½	500	65	116.1	20	60	
Main cables	16 × 4	1256	65	583.1	50	228 (684 × 0.333)	2041
Diagonal braces	4 × 2½	500	65	58.0	20	60	53

★The factor of $\frac{1}{10}$ from Telford's experiments has been applied to produce 60 lb for the cables with a curvature depth of $\frac{1}{50}$ of the span and $\frac{1}{3}$ to produce 228 lb for the main cables of $\frac{1}{20}$ of the span curvature depth.

tons/sq. in. was induced by the self-weight of the cables. This design, based on the inaccurately high 'elastic limit' data, would have been too highly stressed to have provided an adequate safety margin for the bridge. It is difficult to envisage the equalization of stresses taking place uniformly in practice throughout so large a structure.

Work on the project was considered to have matured by September 1814, but finance was not forthcoming, and eventually after a lull of 2 years, much discussion, consideration of other designs and further experiments, a more economical version of the design emerged in July 1817.

Modified bar cable design. The modified design, which can be considered the direct forerunner of Menai Bridge, represented a considerable improvement on its predecessor. The cables under and adjoining the roadway were abandoned, suspension now being solely from the main cables, a change which eliminated the longitudinal sag in the deck. This refinement resulted in considerable saving in ironwork. A further reduction in suspended weight was achieved by adopting a much lighter deck, the result of which with the retention of the previous cable arrangements, had the effect of reducing the maximum design stress to about 11.6 tons/sq. in. Other improvements were the lowering of the cables from 15 to about 7 ft above the roadway at mid-span, whilst maintaining the same cable curvature, and also in achieving a more direct line of anchorage (compare Figs 2 and 8). In the 1814 designs the suspension lines were carried over cast-iron frames of quadrant elevation at each side of the bridge (a development of the 1811 Menai centering proposal towers shown in Fig. 1), from a nearly horizontal alingnment to terminate vertically in the lugs of a large iron casting embodied into masonry.

The modified design was supported by additional experimental work. In May 1817, Telford, Donkin and John Fletcher of Chester, a canal engineer and surveyor, conducted further experiments on the strength of wrought iron at Brunton's works, and continued to obtain results which now seem unrealistically high by about 25%. In one experiment, which is a good example of Telford's practical approach to suspension bridge design, the force required to bring a chain to curvature depths at mid-span of 1/15.6 to 1/20 of its span was determined (Fig. 4). Telford concluded that to achieve a curva-

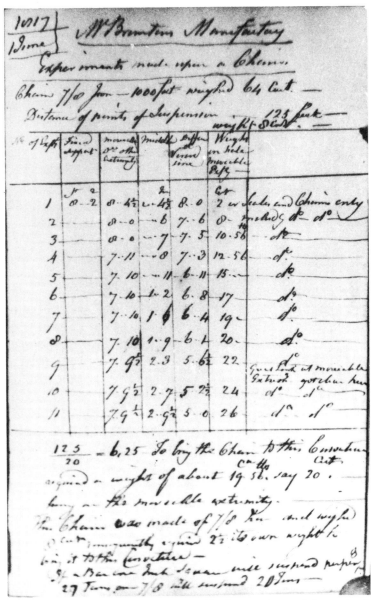

Fig. 4. *Runcorn Bridge project 1817: Telford's experimental determination of force required to bring a suspension chain to different degrees of curvature (Telford notebook, Institution of Civil Engineers)*

ture depth of 1/20 span a force 2½ times the weight of the chain was required, a result he used in 1819 for the Menai Bridge design. Although this figure can be calculated quite readily from theory, Telford placed little reliance on such methods, preferring to proceed on the basis of experiment. This *modus operandi* would be scarcely countenanced as a modern engineering technique but it was undoubtedly sufficiently accurate and prudent at the time in the absence of adequately developed and propagated theoretical methods.

Outcome. Although the estimate of £66 565.15*s* for implementing this design was about 25% less than its predecessor, by May 1818 subscriptions had only reached about £25 000, and the bridge was not built. In fact, about half a century was to pass before Runcorn Gap was eventually spanned by the engineer William Baker, using lattice girders.

The unsatisfactory outcome of the 1814–18 project was very disappointing for the promoters, including Telford and his team, but their efforts were not without effect. As Provis commented, the project established a new era in the art of bridge building and 'the publication of Mr. Telford's design led to the construction of bridges and piers on the suspension principle in almost every part of the kingdom.'[9] In fact, Telford had provided an experimental basis and developed a practicable design for such structures which attracted the support of informed opinion. His experimental results were widely publicized by Barlow of the Royal Military Academy[7] and others. Within a matter of months the opportunity to construct a long-span suspension bridge over Menai Strait occurred, and Telford and Provis, undoubtedly the best qualified engineers of their day for this task, took up the challenge.

In connection with the Runcorn project, mention should be made of the role of Capt. Samuel Brown. Even though he had had very little experience of bridge building at this time, his proposal for the bridge being 'only a sketch of a chain',[9] he was an authority on the design and manufacture of iron chains, the use of which he was anxious to promote. Although Telford did not adopt a long link bar chain of the type developed and promoted by Brown[10] (see Fig. 7), the two men had a useful technical conference relating mainly to the proposed ironwork and timber deck arrangement Brown's support undoubtedly added credibility to the Runcorn

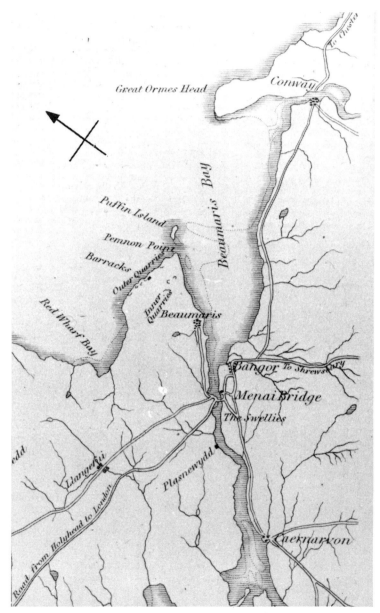

Fig. 5. Menai Strait showing bridge and quarry sites. (Provis, ref. 9, plate 1)

Fig. 6(a). Menai Bridge 1818–19 (Aquatint by J. Taylor). The extent of the design evolution after this period was considerable. The backstays were abandoned in favour of rock anchorages; the towers were increased in height; chains were substituted for cables; and the centre span was increased. The suspenders above the masonry arches were supplied for visual effect and to dampen chain vibration

Fig. 6(b). Menai Bridge elevation as built (J. G. James)

project, which, in turn, created much wider interest in the subject than he had been able to engender with his works model bridge of 1813 or 1814,[11] and helped him to become established as an iron bridge and pier builder.

Menai Bridge, 1818–26

1818–19 cable bridge proposal. In the latter part of 1817 Telford was asked by the Chancellor of the Exchequer to report on the practicability of carrying the Holyhead Road across the Menai Strait on a suspension bridge. In February 1818 he was on site, and by May had proposed an outline plan and report for a sixteen cable bridge at Ynys-y-Moch (Fig. 5) with a 560 ft central chord opening, supported from cast-iron tower frames with backstays tied into the masonry approach arches (Fig. 6(a)). Although Telford considered this proposal practicable and substantial, he forewarned 'I shall certainly during the time the stonework is constructing, claim the privilege of repeating and extending my experiments, in order to arrive at the most perfect mode this principle is susceptible of'.[12] In fact, the design process was almost continuous from 1818 to the completion of the bridge in 1826, the timing of particular design elements being dictated by the progress of other work. This procedure, which resulted in the evolution of a much improved design by allowing more time and, in consequence, greater flexibility in the design process, proved to be very necessary due to the unprecedented nature of the bridge and the technology required for its construction.

In May 1818 Telford and other technical witnesses were called before the Holyhead Road Commissioners to give evidence on the practicability of a suspension bridge. The project received general agreement. At first, Telford proposed to use bar cables (Fig. 3) as the principal means of support; John Rennie preferred chains. Neither Telford nor Rennie thought that there would be any injury to the bridge from wind. Professor Barlow and William Chapman, a Newcastle civil engineer, had made theoretical calculations on the strength of the bridge and gave the proposal their support.

Telford advised that the bridge could be built for £70 000 and within three years. This sum was much lower than the previous estimates for cast-iron bridges, of £127 331 (1811) by Telford and £268 500 (1802) by Rennie. In fact, the bridge took eight years to complete and cost about £178 000[13] exclusive of approach road and ferry compensation (not the usually quoted figure of £120 000), but the structure as built was larger and stronger than originally envisaged.

William Provis was appointed Resident Engineer in June 1818. In August he and the masonry contractors, Straphen and Hall, laid the foundation stone to the Anglesey pier. On 24 April, 1819, Telford reported to the Parliamentary Select Committee for the Holyhead Road that the suspended weight of the bridge

'is 342 tons: by numerous experiments . . . it appears that with a chord line of 560 feet, and a versed sine of 37 (or a curvature of 1/15th) a bar of good iron, one inch square, will, besides its own weight, carry 10½ tons, and about one half of that weight before it begins to stretch. For the Menai Bridge, I have taken a section of 192 square inches, which at 5¼ tons to each square inch, will support 1008 tons.'

To guard against undulation effects he proposed making the roadway sides of framed ironwork. He continued:

'. . . With a bridge 30 feet in breadth, and 532 feet in length there is not much to be apprehended from side vibration . . . contraction or expansion . . . with a difference of 90 degrees of Fahrenheit . . . about 5 inches upon 700 feet . . . The weight of the bridge is 489 tons, upon which, if 300 tons additional are placed, they make 789 tons. The pull of this weight at the abutments . . . is found by my experiments over a pulley . . . equal to about two and a half times the weight on the other side, or 1972 tons.'[14]

In this account there is an inconsistency in that the 'two and a half times' pull relates to a curve with a central deflexion of 1/20 span (Fig. 4) or say 30 ft, in this case, and not the 'versed sine of 37' as he supposed. It seems clear from the application of the experimental result and scaling from the drawing that Telford intended the central deflexion to be 30 ft at this time. The proposed dead load design stress of 5¼ in/sq. in. was much safer than previously proposed and it is evident that Telford had catered for temperature changes, and also, as far as his knowledge would allow, for undulation. Rennie and Donkin were called before the Select Committee and continued to support the proposal, although Rennie advised increasing the strength of the chains by about 20%.

As it transpired, more time was available for design work than

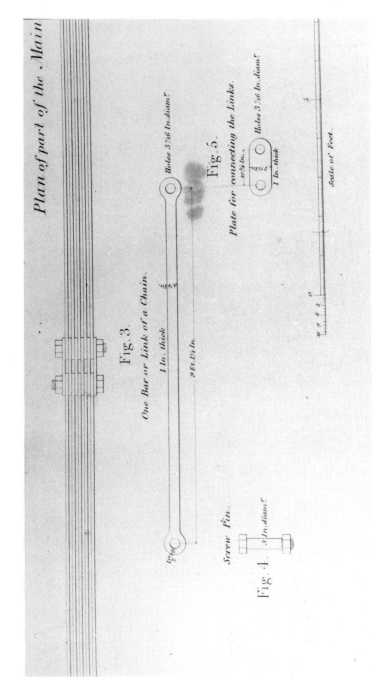

Plan of part of the Main

Fig. 3.
One Bar or Link of a Chain.
1 In. thick

Holes 3⅟₁₆ In. diam.ʳ
9 Ft. 1¼ In.

Fig. 5.
Plate for connecting the Links.
Holes 3⅟₁₆ In. diam.ʳ
1 In. thick

Scale of Feet.

Screw Pin.
Fig. 4. 3 In. diam.ʳ

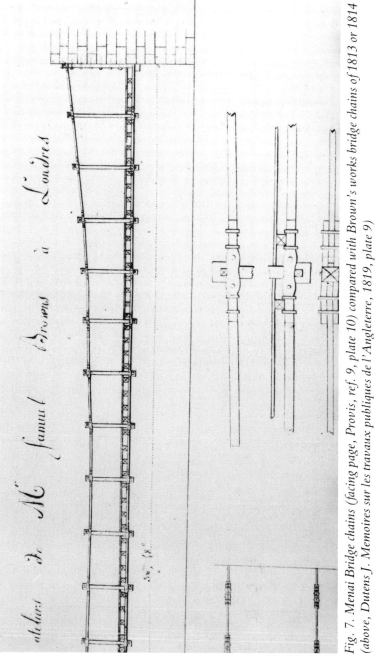

Fig. 7. Menai Bridge chains (facing page, Provis, ref. 9, plate 10) compared with Brown's works bridge chains of 1813 or 1814 (above, Dutens J. Memoires sur les travaux publiques de l'Angleterre, 1819, plate 9)

had been first anticipated because of delay to the masonry work. The hard limestone of which the bridge is built was transported by sea from quarries near Penmon Point, Anglesey (Fig. 5). From 1818 onwards many storms affected delivery of stone shipments and caused delays on the project to be in terms of years. In 1822 alone, three ships, the *Sally* (of 70 tons), the *Alice-Ann* and the *Winsford* were wrecked. The resignation of Straphen and Hall from their contract after only 8 months was another contributory factor to the delay. In 1820 this contract was taken over by John Wilson, one of Telford's principal masonry contractors on the Caledonian Canal works, which by then were substantially complete. It was not until the middle of 1821 that the advance of the masonry work made it necessary to finalize the design of the ironwork.

Design modifications, 1821–23. The principal modifications to the original design included increasing the span to almost 580 ft, raising the towers from 37 ft to 50 ft above the roadway, substituting masonry for cast iron, lengthening the main chains, anchoring them in solid rock, and increasing their cross-sectional area and depth of curvature. With regard to the two latter points, Telford did not consider any change necessary, but deferred to the opinion of Rennie in respect of an increase in cross-sectional area and to that of Davies Gilbert, a mathematician and Holyhead Road Commissioner, and Professor Barlow, for an increase in depth of curvature. A cross-sectional area of 260 sq. in. was adopted and a depth of curvature of 43 ft.

The decision to abandon the composite bar cable in favour of chain bars was taken some time between April 1819 and July 1821, probably in 1820. Telford was undoubtedly influenced in this matter by Captain Brown's eye-bar links, possibly by their successful application at Union Bridge over the Tweed in Berwickshire. He may also have wished to accommodate Rennie's preference for chains. Whatever the reason, the bar link was the most practicable proposition at the time. Telford employed it in a more ingenious way than Brown, by cross-bolting the bars in parallel instead of resting T bar hangers on the top of the individual lines of chain (Fig. 7).

In the latter part of 1822 progress on pier building made necessary the finalization of the saddle and anchorage designs. A comparison between the revised Runcorn Bridge and the improved anchorage in rock at Menai is shown in Fig. 8. The piers had reached roadway level, and before proceeding further it was decided to increase the tower heights by a further 2 ft in order that the roadway at mid-span could be lifted by a similar amount, thus obviating visual unattractiveness due to the deck sagging with temperature changes below a horizontal line. The propriety of this degree of design sensitivity became apparent later, when a winter/summer differential of 11 in. at mid span was observed, associated with a movement of about 1½ in. at each saddle.

The dowelled masonry towers, one of the most remarkable and successful features of the bridge, were completed in 1824. They were designed not only to take the vertical load, but also a significant horizontal force, caused by the angles of the chains being nearly 2° different from the horizontal at each side of the Caernarvonshire tower. This was to allow more headroom on the approach road, which turns under the north chains near the toll house. The expense of the masonry, the most costly single element of the bridge, amounted to about £88 000.

Ironwork

The contract with William Hazeldine for the manufacture and delivery of the ironwork was entered into soon after the drawings had been made in July 1821. The ironwork was manufactured at Upton Forge and finished and tested in Hazeldine's Coleham workshops in Shrewsbury. Most of it was transported via the Ellesmere and Chester Canals and then by sea from Chester to Menai. Every operation in connection with the manufacture, finishing and testing of the ironwork was performed under the control of John Provis, brother of William Provis. The scale of the work was unprecedented. The sixteen main chains were each 1710 ft long and consisted of 14 960 eye-bars about 9½ ft long, some 16 000 connecting plates about 1½ ft long, and 6000 3 in. dia. screw-pins 16 in. long (Fig. 7).

Hazeldine's facilities were originally inadequate to meet the technological challenge of the work, and the first cargo of main chain bars was not delivered at Menai until 31 October, 1822. In the winters of 1822–23 and 1823–24 the forge at Upton was flooded several times. Considerable difficulty was experienced in obtaining bars of the correct length when the holes were hot-formed and from 1823

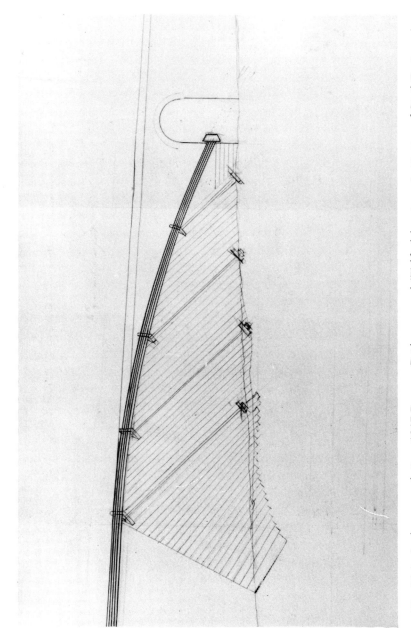

Fig. 8(a). Anchorage evolution: 1817 Runcorn Bridge proposal (Telford drawings, Institution of Civil Engineers)

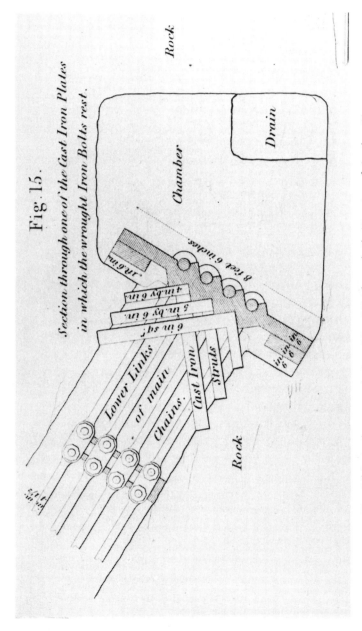

Fig. 15.

Section through one of the Cast Iron Plates
in which the wrought Iron Bolts rest.

Rock

Chamber

Drain

8 feet 6 inches.

4in.6in.

4 in.by 6 in.

5 in. by 6 in.

6 in. sq.

Lower Links
of main
Chains.

Cast Iron
Struts

Rock

Fig. 8(b). Anchorage evolution: Menai Bridge as built (Provis, ref. 9, plate 9)

onwards they were cold-drilled on site using a specially constructed machine. Even so, it did not prove an easy task to achieve the
parallel five-bar chain (Fig. 7). These and other setbacks resulted in
insufficient ironwork being available at the bridge site in the
summer of 1824. In retrospect, Thomas Rhodes, who had previously worked with Telford on the ironwork of the Caledonian
Canal and who supervised the ironwork fixing at Menai Bridge,
thought that link manufacture could be improved in future by turning the pins true, boring the links correctly to length and passing
their ends through a rolling mill.

On 30 June, 1824, the Commissioners expressed concern about
the great delay in finishing the ironwork, and asked Telford to consider and report on whether it might not therefore be advisable to
offer the Conway Bridge ironwork to some other contractor.
However, this did not prove necessary, as the measures taken by
Hazeldine at Shrewsbury, which included provision of new workshops and a large steam engine to power machinery for turning
saddle rollers, punching eyes and cutting screw-pins, were already
taking effect.

Payments to Hazledine for Menai Bridge began about August
1821 and some measure of the difficulties he encountered is reflected in the fact that by December 1822 he had been paid only £2645
from an eventual total of about £68 000. The manufacture and testing of the ironwork was at the forefront of the technology of its
time and resulted in considerable design innovation in respect of a
whole range of equipment (Fig. 9). From the time of the design and
building of the bar tester in 1822 until 1824, the design of equipment for various purposes was virtually a continuous process.
Nothing that could be tested or measured was left to chance. Every
main chain bar and connecting plate was proved by John Provis
with a force of 35 tons (about 11 tons/sq. in.). After testing, the bar
was checked for permanent deformation, and if satisfactory, was
stamped with Provis's proof mark, a raised cross within a ¼ in. dia.
saucer-shaped indentation. Of the 35 649 bars and plates tested,
about 6.7% were discarded. Most of the bars rejected were either
too long or too short, and many of the plates were imperfectly
welded under the forge hammer. A good many of the bars failed
near their ends, probably from repeated heating and cooling whilst
the eyes were being formed.

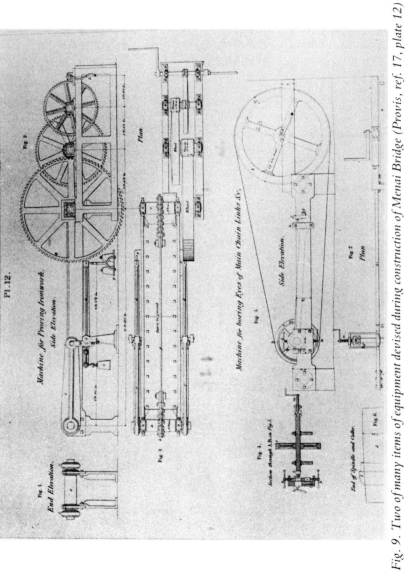

Fig. 9. Two of many items of equipment devised during construction of Menai Bridge (Provis, ref. 17, plate 12)

On 31 March the first anchorage casting was fixed. The most intensive period of ironwork erection began in the spring of 1824. The 1 in. × 3½ in. bars for the side spans were assembled on scaffolding close to their final positions. In the tunnels leading to the anchorages, the chains were fixed from the castings towards the piers to meet the chains fixed from the saddles downwards. On completion of the side spans the chains for the central span were floated out, attached to a tail-end of chain hanging down the face of the Caernarvonshire tower (Fig. 10), and then hoisted up to the saddles

Fig. 10. Caernarvonshire tower immediately before erection of first chain in April 1825 (Provis, ref. 17, plate 4)

on the Anglesey tower by means of specially designed capstans. All sixteen chains were erected between 26 April and 9 July, 1825, nine of them taking less than 2 hours to put up.

Undulation problems and strengthening

Payments to Rhodes in respect of Menai Bridge amounted to about £11 000. About £3200 of this was spent in combatting the effects of the undulation which became apparent almost immediately after the opening of the bridge on 30 January, 1826 – the last phase of the project.

In October 1825 when work was in progress on the deck, Telford had asked Rhodes for a report on side vibration and vertical undulation. Rhodes had observed that when the chains were hanging singly with a gale of wind the vibration was from 6 to 8 in. each way. If the wind struck obliquely the undulation was considerable, but when the chains were connected to the short suspenders these motions were reduced. When the roadway was begun the undulation and vibration was very great and the men had considerable difficulty in standing:

> '. . . the motion resembles much a ship riding at anchor when blowing fresh . . . we are now nailing the first tier of plank down to the roadway bars & at every strake that is fastened I perceive it gets stiffer . . .'[15]

By the end of December, after a storm, the question of additional ironwork was under active consideration. Rhodes suggested restraining the movement of the chains by lines of rods 1 in. square radiating from the corner of the base of the suspension pillar at the roadway. On 4 and 5 January, 1826, more gales occurred, resulting in very considerable undulation, which compelled the workmen to leave the bridge. On 10 February, 48 suspenders were found to be broken at the roadway bar bolt holes (Fig. 11). Several days later a considerable number more were broken. Rhodes suggested the introduction of a pin-jointed section to replace the roadway ends of the suspenders, but this idea was not adopted at that time. Rhodes and Provis believed that gusts of wind first deranged the chains and that deck undulation then followed. Transverse chain bracing was incorporated into the bridge during the early summer of 1826. The maximum undulation in the severest storm before its provision was said to be about 18 in. but afterwards it never exceeded 6 in.

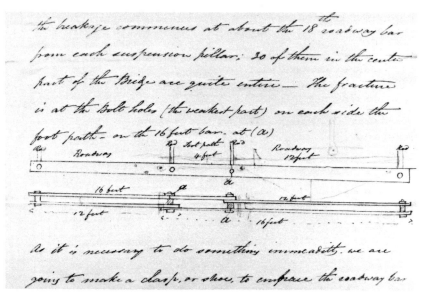

Fig. 11 Rhodes' sketch showing suspender bars fractured at roadway bar bolt holes (a–a), (Letter to Telford, ref. 15)

Henry Palmer, who had assisted Telford during the early years of the project, later confirmed that the probability of deck trussing being required had been foreseen, but that Telford, after anxious consideration, had decided to omit it initially and to adopt it later if necessary. In 1832 the bridge was said to be 'unimpaired and in perfect security',[16] and it was not until 1836, after Telford's death, that further problems arose.

The torsional undulation problems at Menai Bridge made Telford cautious about extending the spans of suspension bridges, although in July 1826 he did propose a road bridge for the Runcorn site with a central opening of 800 ft. For Clifton Bridge, with its deck 200 ft or more above the river, Telford considered 600 ft to be a proper limit to the span. This constraint influenced Brunel's original design for this bridge, which was accepted early in 1831, although shortly afterwards he adopted a span of 702 ft with a suspended roadway length of 636 ft.

Undulation remained a problem even after 1834. During an unusually severe gale at the beginning of January 1836 the Bridgemaster observed deck undulations of 'little less than 16 ft'[17] in amplitude. Provis considered that 10 years of continued friction, combined with timber shrinkage, had considerably affected the original rigidity of the platform. Roadway stiffening was recommended but nothing was done, and in a storm on 7 January, 1839, the deck sustained serious damage. The suspending rods were bent backwards and forwards where they were held fast at the roadway surface, and many broke. Damage to the central footway (which could still be crossed) and to the main chains was slight, three bars being damaged. Rhodes surveyed and reported on the damage to Provis, who prepared plans for a complete reconstruction of the deck. In the meantime immediate repairs were carried out, and 4 days after the storm one carriageway was reopened. By 21 January the whole bridge was open for use.

Work on Provis's deck was in progress by May 1839 and com-

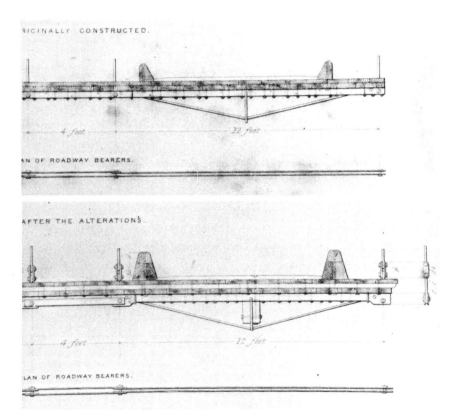

Fig. 12. Part of cross section of original deck and heavier pin-jointed deck of 1839–93. (Maude, ref. 18, plate 17)

pleted in the summer of 1840 at a cost of almost £9000. The new deck was 130 tons heavier than the original: new features included longitudinal stiffening beams under the roadways, hinged cross beams, and pin joints in the suspenders to the roadway surface (Fig. 12).[18] But the problems had a serious psychological effect and it became 'usual for persons to speak of the Menai Bridge as a complete failure'.[19] This was an over-reaction. The cost of the repairs and the heavier deck that Provis had considered necessary amounted to about 5% of the capital cost of the bridge, and of this sum a considerable proportion was for additional work, not replacement. Provis's deck lasted 53 years, not being replaced until 1892, when a steel deck designed by Sir Benjamin Baker was constructed.

Although there were some doubts about the strength of the structure, it was not until 1938–41 that Baker's deck and the main chains were replaced, to a design by Sir Alexander Gibb and Partners. This reconditioning does not seem to have been dictated so much by any structural weakness as by the need for a greater carriageway capacity to deal with the increasing volume of traffic.

The reaction may, however, be understandable. The damage to Menai Bridge in 1836 and 1839 followed a succession of suspension bridge disasters, at Montrose (1830), Morpeth (1830), Broughton (1831), Yore (1831), Stockton railway bridge (c. 1832) and the Brighton Chain Pier (1833). These failures resulted in a disenchantment with this type of bridge design, which seems to have lasted until about the middle of the century. By that time Provis's reconstructed deck at Menai Bridge and J. M. Rendel's substantial longitudinal trussing at Montrose Bridge were proving effective. Another factor which tended to increase confidence in suspension bridges was the success of the Hammersmith Bridge (1824–27), Hungerford footbridge (1841–45) and most of the economical James Dredge stay bridges, of which about 50 had been built between 1836 and 1850. The last of the large span wrought-iron parallel bar chain bridges included the Pesth (Budapest, 1840–49), Portland Street, Glasgow (1851–53) Victoria, Chelsea (1854–58) and Clifton (1830–63).

Influence of Menai Bridge

The Menai Bridge scheme exercised a fundamental influence on the construction and development of suspension bridges from 1818 for several decades. It established this type of bridge in its true role as the most economic means of providing the largest bridge spans for carriage traffic in the western world.

The project also provided a basis for improvements in suspension bridge design both by example and through the publications of its designers and others, including Gilbert,[20] Navier,[21] and Cresy.[22] The development of underground solid rock anchors represented a significant step forward. The parallel bar chain had the advantage over Brown's arrangement that it was more easily adapted to large cross-sectional areas and to the catenary of uniform strength. Leading designers, including W. T. Clark and I. K. Brunel, subsequently adopted and, assisted by developments in iron technology and structural theory, improved on the basic Menai Bridge chain for at least six major bridges during the following three decades.

The Menai Bridge project influenced the adopting of greater and consequently more efficient depths of curvature in suspension bridge chains and also safer chain strengths. In 1814 Telford and Brown adopted shallow curvature depths of main chain in the range 0.02 to 0.05 of the span at mid-span, believing that this practice would minimize the effects of vibration and the uncertainties and expense of providing adequate towers. For small spans Telford's practice differed from Brown's, the degree of curvature of the main cables for a proposed bridge at Latchford in 1814 (0.07 span) being about three times more efficient in strength terms than the chains of Brown's work bridge (0.032 span). The published chain curvature depth given by Telford for the mid-span of the 1818–19 Menai Bridge design was 1/15 (0.056 span). From 1821 onwards most designers, including Brown, adopted curvature depths in the range 0.066–0.10 of the span, which represented a significant improvement.

During the second decade of the 19th century there was a considerable variation of practice in respect of superimposed loading and design stresses, some of the latter probably being beyond the yield point of wrought iron. Telford's adoption in 1818 of a dead load maximum stress of about 6 tons/sq. in. (9.8 tons/sq. in. with 300 tons live load) represented a significant step forward. In 1821 these stresses were further reduced to about 4.3 and 6.3 tons/sq. in. respectively. Although Brown seems to have been influenced to some extent by this downwards trend in his Union Bridge designs, he adopted maximum stresses nearly double those of Telford thereafter, and at least two of his bridges, Montrose and Stockton, suffered from overstressing of their main chains. In 1829 Brunel considered 8 tons/sq. in. as a maximum working stress, but in 1830 reduced this to 6.5 tons (almost the Menai Bridge figure), and eventually in 1838 to 5.0 tons/sq. in. Navier took a great interest in the Menai Bridge project and adopted an almost identical span and chain curvature for his Paris suspension bridge of 1823–26.

The instructive example of the effects of undulation obtained by observation and through the authoritative accounts of Provis, influenced development work towards a solution of the problem by Clark, Rendel, Barlow, Brunel and Provis himself. For Hammersmith Bridge, completed in 1827, Clark made and wind-tested a model and devised an arrangement of longitudinal timber and iron trussing. Brunel, who had observed Menai Bridge in a storm, believed that chain vibration commenced before the platform moved and that the unequal length of the suspension rods then caused the undulatory motion. In 1830 he did not consider longitudinal stressing to be necessary for Clifton Bridge, but by 1840 his drawings show timber longitudinal girders.

The example of Menai Bridge also influenced and encouraged the development of theoretical investigations into suspension bridge design. Ware's theoretical investigations[23] and particularly his catenary tables, facilitated suspension bridge calculation from 1822, and Gregory promoted their use in his books of 1825 and 1833.[24] The most significant development was Gilbert's work, and his approximations for determining the forces in a chain curve at any point have continued in use into the present century. Hodgkinson's theoretical investigations and calculations of 1828 relating to Menai Bridge[25] were also of significance in the propagation of a more scientific approach to design. Developments up to 1832 were summarised and evaluated by Drewry in the first British text book devoted to suspension bridges.[16] From c. 1825 onwards there was a gradual but increasing awareness of the value of a more theoretical approach to suspension bridge design which began to be reflected in the training and practice of the new generation of civil engineers.

In 1838, during the period when suspension bridges were out of favour, the editor of *The Civil Engineer and Architect's Journal* commented that:

> . . . when the material of the suspension portion of the Menai Bridge shall have perished and consigned to ruin . . . by atmospheric agents . . . the granite bridges of London and Waterloo will then exist in the same freshness and vigour of duration as . . . the ancient granite monuments of Egypt.'[26]

The passage of time has shown otherwise. The foundations of these fine Rennie bridges eventually proved inadequate for the increasing demands made on them, and it is Menai Bridge, albeit skillfully and sympathetically reconditioned, which has survived. Unlike these London bridges it was built at the frontiers of technology and theoretical knowledge, and is today a fitting national monument to the enterprise, courage and dedication of all concerned with its construction and subsequent preservation.

References
 1. Finley J. A description of the patent chain bridge. *The Portfolio*, Philadelphia, 1810, New series 3.
 2. Papers relating to a bridge over the Menai Strait. British Parliamentary Papers (BPP), 1819, 5, 4.
 3. Telford T. Report to the Treasury respecting the great Road from Holyhead through North Wales. 22 April, 1811. Report from the Committee on Holyhead Roads, 30 May, 1811. BPP, 1810–11, 3, 27–28.
 4. Rickman J. (ed). *Life of Thomas Telford*. London, 1838.
 5. Telford T. Report respecting Runcorn Bridge . . . 13 March, 1817. Report of Select Committee, Warrington, 1817.
 6. *Ibid.*, Supplementary report, 22 July, 1817.
 7. Barlow P. *An essay on the strength and stress of timber.* London, 1817.
 8. Calculations: Runcorn Bridge, dimensions and estimate, 1814. Telford Mss, Ironbridge Gorge Museum Trust (almost certainly in the hand of W. A. Provis with annotations by Telford).
 9. Provis W. A. *An historical and descriptive account of the suspension bridge constructed over the Menai Strait.* London, Provis, 1828, 16.
10. Brown S. Ms patent (Scottish). Scottish Records Office, Edinburgh, C/20/18/15.
11. Brown S. On the proposed plan of erecting a patent wrought iron bridge of suspension over the Thames. *Tech. Repos.*, 1824, 5, 292.
12. Rickman, *op. cit*; also *op. cit.* ref. 2.

13. Compiled from Ms T/HO 92, pp 94–5, Telford Mss, Institution of Civil Engineers and Holyhead Road Commissioners Accounts, Public Records Office, Work 6, 83.
14. 3rd Report of Select Committee on the road from London to Holyhead. BPP, 1819, 5, 25–26.
15. Rhodes to Telford, 10 Feb., 1826. Telford Mss Lr, Institution of Civil Engineers.
16. Drewry C. S. *A memoir on suspension bridges*. London, Longmans, 1832.
17. Provis W. A. Observations on the effects produced by wind on the suspension bridge over the Menai Strait. *Trans. Instn Civ. Engrs*, 1842, 3, 360.
18. Maude T. J. An account of alterations to Menai Bridge. *Trans. Instn Civ. Engrs*, 1842, 3, plate XVII.
19. *Civ. Engr Arch. Jnl*, 1845, 8, 250.
20. Gilbert D. On some properties of the catenarian curve with reference to bridges by suspension. *Quart. Jnl Sci. roy. Instn*, 1821, 10, Jan., 230–235.
21. Navier C. L. M. H. *Rapport a Monsieur Becquey . . . et mémoir sur les ponts suspendus*. Paris, Imprimerie Royale, 1823.
22. Cresy E. *An encyclopaedia of civil engineering*. 1847.
23. Ware S. *Tracts on vaults and bridges*, 1822, 3.
24. Gregory O. *Mathematics for practical men*. London, Baldwin, Cradock and Joy, 1825, 1833.
25. Hodgkinson E. A few remarks on the Menai Bridge. *Mem. Lit. phil. Soc. Manchester*, 1831, 5, 2nd series, 545–53.
26. *Civ. Engr Arch. Jnl*, 1838, 1, 317.

6

Telford and steam carriages

ANGUS DALGLEISH

Telford is famous for his work as an architect and as an engineer who created structures of a scale not envisaged in the western world since the great days of the Roman Empire. Yet his interests were not solely in the design and construction of these works. Not surprisingly in one of his attainments, he was also much concerned with the use made of them, although his independence of mind did not allow him to be associated with any project in which he did not believe. His life spanned a great age of road and canal building, and much of his work related to these two forms of transport. What is less well known is the extent to which mechanical power had been developed during this period and applied to the propulsion of road vehicles.

The common belief is that mechanically propelled vehicles first came into general use at the end of the 19th century when the 'red flag' legislation was repealed; yet quite sophisticated steam powered vehicles were running on our roads 60 years earlier. In 1831 steam carriages were familiar enough on the common roads and turnpikes for highly discriminatory charges to have been imposed upon them by the turnpike trusts. These were usually at least six times greater than those for stage coaches.

By 1824, and after a visit by an assistant to the Stockton and Darlington Railway, Telford had noted a fundamental disadvantage of rail transport: that all traffic would have to be handled by the company which owned the line. At that time it was accepted without question that any route – waterway or turnpike road – should be freely open to anyone who wished to use it, on payment of a statutory toll. The canal companies were forbidden to trade on their own canals. This was a most valuable rule for the avoidance of monopoly. The coming of railways, with their requirement for the trains to operate to rigid timetables, meant that this rule had to go. It is a remarkable tribute to Telford's prescience that he had grasped this so early.

Telford considered that steam power could best be applied to land transport in the form of road vehicles able to run anywhere on the network of common roads, as well as on turnpikes which might be specially built for them. While agreeing that railways could be a practical form of transport, he considered them to be inherently uneconomic. He could not see the merit in a machine which required a costly special track reserved for its exclusive use, and which restricted its range of movement, a point which transportation engineers are only now beginning to appreciate.

Telford saw railways as an adjunct to a canal system, for use where the land was unfavourable to canal construction or where water supplies were inadequate. In this he has been vindicated by time and experience in the USA: there the railroads are highly profitable for long haul movement of bulk materials, this being on a scale barely comprehended in the UK. USA railroads run trainloads of 10 000 tons or more over distances of 2000 miles: but where the waterways have been extensively developed for navigation, the railroads cannot compete even for such long hauls.

Parliamentary investigations

The scandal of the toll charges led, with Telford's support, to the setting up in 1831 of a Parliamentary Select Committee to investigate them and to determine a fair basis for levying tolls on steam carriages. The Committee was also given a second task of greater significance:

> '. . . to inquire generally into the present state and future prospects of Land Carriage by means of Wheeled Vehicles propelled by Steam or Gas on common roads and to report upon the probable utility which the Public may derive therefrom.'

The Committee took evidence from highway engineers, from those who promoted, designed and operated steam carriages, and from engineers and others who had studied the economics of mechanical transport and who were able to give an informed opinion on the benefits to be anticipated from its adoption. One of the latter was Colonel Torrens, an MP, who was 'well known for his intelligence and research on subjects connected with the interests of society'.

He stated that each horse in draft on the common roads (the number was estimated to be 1 million) ate the food of eight men, and if this were available to people it would lead to cheaper food, 'an increased industrious population', and to England becoming 'more extensively the workshop of the World'.

The highway engineers were unanimous that injury to the road surface from the action of horses' feet exceeded that caused by the wheels of traffic by a factor of three. This was so, even though the wheels of horse-drawn coaches and carts were made as narrow as possible to reduce tractive effort, which in turn caused rutting. In contrast, the steam carriages had wide tyres for adhesion, an inch of width for each ton of loading being suggested as appropriate.

Telford himself gave evidence briefly. He confirmed the damaging effect of horses' feet, and stated that on a properly made road the carriage wheels had a negligible effect. He considered that steam carriages should not be charged more than horse-drawn ones, but ought in justice to be charged less.

In its unanimous Report to Parliament the Committee recommended limits on the tolls on steam carriages. After considering various possibilities, including tolls based on the number of passengers or the weight or horsepower of the vehicle, they suggested for carriages with up to six passengers the toll should be that for a two-horse carriage, with seven or more passengers the same as for a four-horse carriage. When carrying goods the toll for each ton of load should be the same as that for a one-horse cart.

From the evidence given on 'the present state and future prospects' of this form of transport, it was obvious that there had been much detailed development (Fig. 1). Advanced boiler design minimized the volume of steam which could escape on a burst. They had embryonic forms of flash boiler, with the area exposed to fire very large in relation to the overall dimensions: one had 250 sq. ft. of heating surface in a 25 cu. ft. boiler. Cylinders were jacketed for efficiency. Forced draught fans were used in preference to induced draught, the injection of exhaust steam into the chimney as on a railway engine being considered too noisy. Blow-off steam was discharged into the fire-box to avoid nuisance. Boilers had fusible plugs as well as safety valves. They even fitted a 'dead man's pedal'

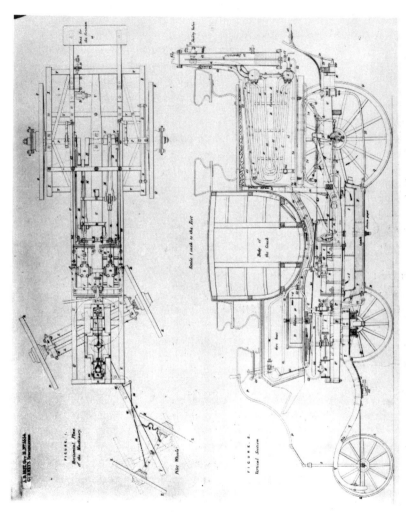

Fig. 2. Gurney steam coach, from a print of 1827 (Imperial Science Museum)

which disconnected the valve gear if the driver lifted his foot.
Richard Trevithick produced a complex design for a condensing
engine which he had patented. Yet an expert witness considered
those steam coaches to be 'mere experiments'.

Braking was by band brake on the tyre, or by reversing the valve
gear. In either case the wheel did not lock and did far less damage
than the drags used on horse drawn vehicles. A strange sidelight on
early development was Gurney's statement that his 1825 carriage
was equipped with 'propellers' or 'feet' (Fig. 2) as he thought friction between wheels and road would be inadequate, but after his
carriage went up Highgate Hill without using them (Fig. 3), the
feet were removed in 1826. From their evidence most operators
drove one wheel only, connecting the second in exceptional circumstances, so wheel-slip was not a problem. Gurney, in fact, in
1829 drove from London to Bath and back using only one wheel.
Hancock (Fig. 4) was experimenting with gearing for use on hills
instead of the usual direct drive.

A witness estimated that steam carriages could be run for one-
third of the cost of horse-drawn coaches: costs for the latter
increased very rapidly with increased speed. Another advantage
claimed for steam was safety: there was no danger of being run
away with, and that of being overturned was greatly diminished. A
steam carriage could be stopped or turned 'with the slightest exertion, under circumstances where horses would be totally un-
manageable'. The danger of road accidents from horse-drawn
traffic is often overlooked by those who regard the 19th century as
a golden age compared with today. In the 1860s, when all but local
travel was by rail and the population was far less mobile, the numbers of road deaths in relation to the population were not so greatly
different from those of today.

A speed of 24 mile/h had been maintained over a 4 mile run, and
an average of 12 mile/h over much longer distances. This does not
appear to have alarmed the passengers: one promoter, Nathaniel
Ogle, reported 'we have had whole families of ladies, day after day,
out with us in all directions, and who have the most perfect confidence.'

Summing up, the Report concluded:

That carriages can be propelled by steam on common roads at an
average rate of ten miles per hour

Fig. 3. Gurney's steam carriage at Highgate Tunnel (Imperial Science Museum)

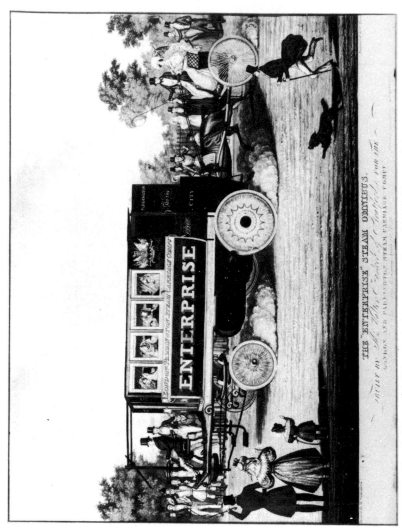

Fig. 4. Hancock's 'Enterprise' steam omnibus of 1833 (Imperial Science Museum

That at this rate they have conveyed upwards of fourteen passengers

That their weight, including engine, fuel, water and attendants, may be under three tons

That they can ascend and descend hills of considerable inclinations with facility and safety

That they are perfectly safe for passengers

That they are not (or need not be if properly constructed) nuisances to the public

That they will become a speedier and cheaper mode of conveyance than carriages drawn by horses

That, as they admit of greater breadth of tire than other carriages, and as the roads are not acted on so injuriously as by the feet of horses in common draught, such carriages will cause less wear of roads than coaches drawn by horses

That rates of toll have been imposed on steam carriages which would prohibit their being used on several lines of road, were such charges permitted to remain unaltered.

As regards tolls, the Committee recommended to Parliament that legislative protection be extended to steam carriages with the least possible delay. However, the 'prejudices which always beset a new invention' proved too powerful. From today's experience of the lobbies which always arise to oppose new developments, we can well imagine what happened. The many interests – corn merchants, harness makers, horse-copers, railway promoters, iron masters hoping to make rails, and those who were simply against change – would unite against steam carriages. It was only necessary for Parliament to do nothing for them to be killed off, and nothing is what it did. In view of the bitter struggle over the first Reform Bill then in progress, perhaps this is not surprising.

Telford's interest

In spite of this, Telford and his associates did not give up. In the last years of his life they were active in promoting a company, referred to in correspondence simply as the Steam Company, to initiate and run a service of steam carriages on an improved road between London and Birmingham. No doubt it would have been extended to Holyhead as Sir Henry Parnell, one of the 100 Irish MPs who came to Westminster following the union of the British and Irish parliaments in 1800 and a Minister in Lord Grey's government, was interested.

Two of Telford's colleagues, John Macneill and A. M. Robertson, were heavily involved in surveying the route and raising support from interested parties along it. Unpublished letters from them to Telford, now in the Telford collection of the Ironbridge Gorge Museum Trust, and from which only extracts are given here, indicate how intense was the activity.

Initially support was canvassed from innkeepers, coachmasters and canal proprietors. The chief opponent was, of course, the railway, but Macneill writing 20 October, 1833, from Stow refers triumphantly to:

'the present tottering state of the rail-way, which appears to be thrown into a state of confusion by the fact, (which has just come out) that they will be obliged to go to Parliament for a new line, between Coventry and Watford . . . Their shares are coming down rapidly.'

He also describes the road as 'in a very good state . . . except the first 25 miles out of London, but even that is not very bad'.

Five days later he is writing from Coventry:

'The Roads are at present in excellent order and all the Surveyors, Innkeepers and Coach Proprietors are most anxious for our success. Mr Freath gave 10 pounds for the Birmingham Canal and Mr Eyre Lee has written to Lord Clive to get £10 from the Liverpool Junction Canal, and £10 from the Ellesmere Canal so that we shall have ample funds.'

In contrast

'. . . the Railway people are at *logerheads* with one another and . . . very little of the 2nd call has been taken up. The Surveyor whom they have employed is *not likely to do them much good* but he has undertaken the work very low; this shows the state of their finances, for formerly their Surveyors travelled and lived like Noblemen.'

Not all was easy, however. The co-operation of landowners was vital, and on 8 November, Macneill is reporting:

'I found there was so much conflicting interests, along the Road, both amongst the Trustees Clerks, and Surveyors, that without I could make friends of all parties there was little more in anything I could do. – the Landed Interest along the Road through Buckinghamshire, Northamptonshire, etc, etc, place great faith in Mr Brunton, in fact he leads them; to *Good* or *evil*; I therefore endeavoured to bring him into my views, in which I have completely succeeded.'

Macneill was also of the opinion that to consolidate support for the Steam Company a successful trial trip between London and Birmingham was essential. The vehicle chosen was Sir Charles Dance's 'Squire'. Sir Charles had earlier run a service four times a day between Cheltenham and Worcester, carrying 3000 passengers over a 4 month period.

After some delay to put out supplies of fuel along the route and to collect a group of distinguished passengers, including the Clerk to the House of Commons, John Rickman, the trip took place at the beginning of November 1833. They had hoped that Parnell would come, but he had to go off to Edinburgh. Bryan Donkin, another distinguished engineer of the period was also invited; he had had doubts about the excursion, but his letter to Telford indicates that '. . . in consequence of being assured of the pleasure of your company I am determined to risk all consequences and I will attend you personally at 4 on Monday morning. May fire and water befriend us!'

The trial was not a total success. Beyond Highgate a boiler tube failed and there were delays in getting a new one from Maudslay's manufactory, so that they only reached Stoney Stratford on the first day, a journey of 54 miles. Next day the repair was found to be still unsatisfactory and the trip was abandoned, it being considered that the practicability of the journey had been sufficiently demonstrated.

The prospectus of the Steam Company was published in December 1833 and by the end of that month the shares were 'on the move'. At the beginning of February 1834 the shares were still selling – the bulk of the money as reported by Robertson coming from Dublin – and Macneill was agreeing the text of the necessary Parliamentary Bill with the Turnpike Trustees. But on 1 February Robertson wrote to Telford 'I am confident we have no chance of success until a carriage has performed the journey in unequivocal style'.

The organization was also experiencing difficulties in finding suitable carriages. Maudslay's were apparently commissioned to manufacture these but there were delays, and in the same letter Robertson reports:

Macneill & I visited Dr Church who shewed us his carriage which he says will be out in three weeks. He has however already met with an accident to his Boiler, and the whole machine is so large and unwieldy that Macneill thinks it will never be able to move quicker than four miles an hour. It is calculated to carry *150* passengers'.

What happened to the Company after early 1834 I do not know. At the end of January the Duke of Wellington, as Lord Warden of the Cinque Ports, had asked Telford to inspect Dover Harbour which was becoming blocked by shingle: he could hardly refuse. He reported on this in February. On the Birmingham and Liverpool Junction Canal the Shelmore Bank was slipping again and Telford paid a last visit to it in March.

To get the Steam Company on the road would have taken all Telford's prestige and drive; but even as an old sick man he was not left quietly to concentrate on this. Telford died in September 1834 and with him died mechanized road transport, not to be resurrected for 60 years.

What would have happened if either Parliament had legislated on the tolls or Telford's Steam Company had been successful? The conclusion of the Parliamentary Committee's report was that

'These inquiries have led the Committee to believe that the substitution of inanimate for animal power, in draught on common roads, is one of the most important improvements in the means of internal communication ever introduced. Its practicality they consider to have been fully established; its general adoption will take place more or less rapidly in proportion as the attention of scientific men shall be drawn by public encouragement to further improvement.'

There can be little doubt that a network of good toll roads would have soon been built to take the new vehicles and these might be serving the UK today in place of the 20 000 miles of railway which were in fact built. At the end of the 19th century, with railways at the peak of their prestige, engineers could not believe that Telford had opposed them, and tried to make out he had not, since it was almost like being opposed to virtue. But he did oppose railways, and I believe that he has been proved right.

7

Managerial organization on the Caledonian Canal
1803–22

ALASTAIR PENFOLD

Proposals for constructing a canal through the Great Glen were made throughout the 18th century. In 1773 James Watt surveyed the line for the Commissioners of the Forfeited Estates, proposing a canal 10 ft deep at a cost of £164 000. John Knox pressed for its building in his survey of the highlands in 1784, as did local ministers in their contributions to the 'Statistical Account of Scotland' in the 1790s. Pressure came also from the British Fisheries Society, and John Rennie was commissioned to do further survey work in 1793. Continuing agitation from the Highland Society and the British Fisheries Society, combined with mounting anxiety over emigration, caused the Treasury to send Telford on a survey of the highlands in 1801. His involvement with Sir William Pulteney and the British Fisheries Society, undoubtedly helped him in this commission.

He was instructed by the Treasury to select the most suitable sites for fishing stations on the West Coast, to plan road and bridge communications on and between the mainland and islands, and to examine the possibility of constructing a canal through the Great Glen. Telford reported favourably to the Treasury and was sent back the following year. A select Committee was appointed in 1803 to consider his proposals, recommending that they be implemented as soon as possible. In the summer of 1803 Parliament approved the creation of a board of Commissioners to supervise the expenditure of an annual grant of public money for canal construction.

Acts of Parliament were obtained in 1803–04 and full scale canal construction commenced in the summer of 1804. The canal was opened in a very unfinished state in 1822, mainly to pacify mounting criticism over escalating costs. Telford's involvement in the project after that date was confined to compiling annual reports. The Board of Commissioners continued in existence until 1920.

Problems of managerial control were increased on the Caledonian Canal by distance, supply of raw materials and the unprecedented scale of the project. This paper will attempt to describe the managerial structure developed by Telford in response to the above problems, with special reference to the division of responsibility between Telford, Jessop, site engineers and contractors, and the contrast between survey and construction personnel.

The managerial team employed on the construction of the canal remained essentially unaltered throughout much of the construction period, both with regard to personnel and structure. To ensure clarity a brief diagramatic outline of the structure is given in Fig. 1.

Telford and Jessop

Telford and Jessop were both involved in the setting up and running of the managerial team and played a role in the overall project. In assessing their differing contributions it is necessary to answer the following points: who was responsible for the recruitment and, therefore, size of the managerial team; who decided their responsibilities; who assessed wage and contract rates; who decided what

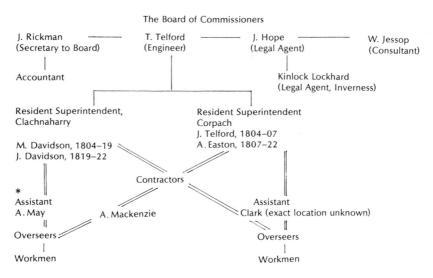

Fig. 1. Managerial structure

materials should be used; who appointed the contractors; and who implemented changes in design and line?

Jessop, together with Rennie, gave evidence before the select committee on the various Highland improvement schemes in June 1803, prior to the creation of the Board of Commissioners.[1] When asked to comment on Telford's proposals for the canal, he stated that he could not give 'an accurate judgement, not having seen the country'. However, he did provide an estimated cost of the whole project, of about £22 000/mile 'under the favourable circumstances of ground tolerably even, and the soil moderately good'.[2] As in the London Bridge enquiry, he was called upon by the Government to give his opinion on the feasibility of the project as one of the country's leading civil engineers. On 4 August, 1803, the newly-appointed Board of Commissioners took measures

'for obtaining the opinion and assistance of Mr William Jessop, another eminent and experienced engineer'.[3]

He was ordered to inspect the proposed line of canal with Telford,[4] which he did in October 1803, reporting back to the Board in February 1804.[5] A revised estimate was also submitted by him at this date. After 1804 he made a joint inspection with Telford in October or November of every year up to his retirement in 1813. He died in 1814.

Recruitment of managerial staff began in the early autumn of 1803 when Telford appointed John Wilson as Resident Engineer or Superintendent at Corpach, and A. May and W. Mackenzie as Superintendent/Pay Clerk at Clachnaharry.[6] These appointments were made before Jessop had become involved with the project.[7] It is probable that John Wilson was the same Wilson who had worked with Telford on Pontcysyllte Aqueduct as a contractor. Nothing is known about the background of Andrew May or William Mackenzie except that the latter was a land surveyor from Inverness. J. Smith was employed at Corpach to negotiate the purchase of country timber and arrange for its cutting and delivery.[8] A Mr Mason was employed to investigate the location of quarries. He was also involved in the preparation of a report on the entrances to the canal with Murdoch Downie.[9] A considerable number of surveying assistants was also taken on,[10] so that by the time of Jessop's visit in October 1803 a full-scale survey team was in operation.

Construction work commenced on a very limited scale in December 1803, but it was not until the passing of the Second Canal Act in June 1804 that moves were made to appoint permanent supervisory construction staff. Jessop was again excluded from the major decision-making over recruitment, simply endorsing Telford's appointments. Evidence for this belief comes from the Second Caledonian Canal Report which contains extracts from Telford and Jessop's correspondence over the new posts. The Commissioners reported that after having

> 'taken into consideration a representation made to us by Mr. Telford respecting the propriety of providing a constant superintendence on the spot, we appointed Mr. Mathew Davidson . . . (Clachnaharry District) . . . and Mr. John Telford . . . (Corpach District) . . . These persons were recommended to us by Mr. Thomas Telford, with the entire approbation and concurrence of Mr. Jessop, as men of tried ability and long experience.'[11]

Telford received authorization from the Board to appoint them.[12] He had written to Jessop on 8 June, 1804, suggesting John Telford and Davidson:

> 'The works being upon a scale of uncommon magnitude, and in a district of country unaccustomed to operations of this nature, I propose that such persons only shall be instructed with the chief superintendence and the execution of the principle works, as have to my own and your knowledge, for ten years past, been employed upon works of a similar nature whose abilities may be relied on and who are likely to enter with zeal into the spirit of the undertaking. . .'[13]

Telford had known Davidson virtually all his life, working with him as a stonemason in his native Eskdale before leaving for London in 1782. He had employed Davidson as site engineer on several bridge projects in Shropshire before appointing him Resident Engineer for Pontcysyllte Aqueduct.[14] Jessop had been Principal Engineer on the project and had become acquainted with Davidson. However, it is evident from the above correspondence that Telford and not Jessop appointed him. Similarly, John Telford was an ex-Telford Ellesmere Canal employee who had been fully versed in his working methods, acting as his personal assistant for some time.[15] Telford concluded his letter of 8 June by proposing that Davidson be provided with 'such assistants for counting the men and measuring the works as may from time-to-time appear necessary'.[16] For the middle district he proposed to employ 'persons of an inferior description' because 'the works there can be occasionally examined and checked by Mathew Davidson and John Telford'.[17] Jessop replied to Telford's proposals on 9 June, agreeing to all the appointments.[18] He made no amendments to the managerial team as suggested by Telford.

Wilson, May and Mackenzie were relieved of their supervisory posts during the ensuing months, Wilson re-emerging as one of the principal contractors, and May as assistant and pay clerk to Mathew Davidson. Mackenzie appears to have left the employment of the Commissioners altogether. Wilson's assistant continued to serve him in his new capacity,[19] (his name appears on wage certificates after 1804). It is not known how much Telford was involved in these reappointments, and details are extremely scarce of Telford and Jessop's involvement in the appointment of managerial staff below the level of superintendent. Jessop requested that Telford deal with the appointment of all assistants in June 1804.

'What Assistants they may want cannot at present be specified, they must from time to time be appointed as circumstances may call for them and this should be left to your discretion'.[20]

Telford and Hope decided upon the appointment of Kinlock Lockhart as the Commissioners' legal representative in Inverness in 1805.[21] Jessop does not appear to have been consulted. John Telford died suddenly in 1807 and was replaced by Alexander Easton, a former stone mason and Telford road inspector in Argyll.[22] Again Jessop does not appear to have been involved. No further managerial appointments appear to have been made before Jessop's retirement in 1813. Telford made Mathew Davidson the senior superintendent, appointing him as his deputy with responsibility for handling all financial matters for the canal when he left for Sweden in 1808.

It is clear that Telford, rather than Jessop, was responsible for managerial recruitment. He was more in touch with the day-to-day running of the canal and therefore better able to devise and appoint a managerial team for its supervision. In this instance at least, Jessop merely rubber stamped Telford's decisions.

Responsibilities

It was Telford, rather than Jessop, who decided upon the responsibilities of the managerial team. In his letter to Jessop of June 1804 Telford proposed that the superintendents fix contract rates in 'particular places' with the proviso that the 'state of such rates . . . be always immediately communicated to me and to be subject to my determination'.[23] Through such a system he undoubtedly hoped to control from a distance by financial manipulation. Telford requested that Jessop comment on the 'above proposal' and hoped that it gave 'a reasonable prospect of the works being carried on with economy, fidelity and success'.[24] No records survive of Jessop either opposing Telford's managerial team or suggesting improvements. It was, therefore, Telford's set of instructions which was adopted by the Board and used on all subsequent occasions for the control of site construction staff.

Jessop's participation in the fixing of contract and wage rates was considerable, as he accompanied Telford on the inspection tours when these matters were considered. He was not involved, however, in deciding the wage rates for the excavation of Corpach and Clachnaharry basins, which had been determined by Telford in 1803.[25] This work had presumably been performed by direct labour, as no contractors were appointed until June 1804 when Telford and Jessop received instructions to 'determine the rates of expense of the sundry works upon the line of canal . . . [and the price of] labour for the different sorts of work.'[26] Telford had contacted the Board of Commissioners in June 1804 requesting Jessop's assistance on the above points:

'It would be a great satisfaction to my mind, to have the assistance and advice of Mr. Jessop in Scotland'.[27]

Immediately after, Telford contacted Jessop, giving him a full breakdown of his proposals:

'Every part of the works which can be so managed, to be executed by measure of rates or prices, to be determined by you or myself after having maturely weighed every circumstance relative to the different works. All the cutting, puddlings and embankments to be let in small lots to different persons, . . . the general rules for prices to be determined by you or myself'.[28]

The various rates were fixed in August 1804 after a joint inspection. Telford and Jessop had previously been instructed to take careful consideration of local wage rates in deciding upon those for the canal.[29] This would suggest that those members of the managerial team who had been in the Highlands longest and therefore had a greater local knowledge (i.e. Telford) played the decisive role in the fixing of wages. This has to be counterbalanced, however, by the fact that Jessop had a far greater knowledge of wage rates throughout the country. Any substantial increase in the contract price was subject to approval by Telford and Jessop.[30] This policy was adhered to throughout Jessop's involvement in the project and beyond. Jessop's contribution to the fixing of prices would thus appear to have been considerable both in 1804 and after. It is not known how much he was influenced by Telford's fixing of wage rates in the autumn of 1803 or by his superior local knowledge.

Materials

In the location, purchase and transport of materials it would again appear that Telford provided the driving force. The survey team was fully involved in this department before Jessop set foot in the Highlands, Telford opening negotiations with Cameron of Lochiel for the purchase of country timber in late September 1803.[31] In the joint instructions of 1803 and 1804, Telford and Jessop were requested to pay special attention to the location of materials.[32] As in previous instances, however, the person with the most local knowledge had the greater say in deciding such matters.

By the summer of 1804 Telford had completed his third 'period of duty' in the Highlands; Jessop was just arriving for his second. Decisions regarding the purchase of timber may have been taken jointly, but it was Telford who handled all the initial enquiries and correspondence. Jessop was probably very influential in the purchase of ironwork, although here again it was Telford who handled the correspondence, shipping and erection. Contracts for ironwork were put out to tender, the offers made by Outram and Co. (Jessop's partner) and Hazledine being accepted. Hazledine had for some time been associated with Telford projects, providing the ironwork for the Pontcysyllte Aqueduct and many of Telford's bridges.

Machinery requirements were decided on at the joint inspection
of August 1804 and orders were placed almost immediately afterwards for three Boulton and Watt pumping engines and a large
amount of plateway.[33] The canal's first dredging machine appears
to have been designed entirely by Jessop,[34] who was probably
instrumental in the adoption of a steam dredger. Telford did not
involve himself in the development of dredging machines after
Jessop's departure, preferring to import specialized knowledge on
the matter, in the person of Bryan Donkin.[35]

Contractors

The choice of construction contractors was made by Telford in
June 1804. In that month he wrote to Jessop suggesting Simpson,
Wilson and Cargill as the masonry contractors.

> 'In all matters relative to the execution of building I mean to employ
> John Simpson with whose abilities and character you have also been
> acquainted for upwards of ten years past. John Wilson and James Cargill
> are with him . . .'[36]

Jessop 'heartily concluded with Telford in appointing the contractors straight away rather than open the contract to competition
[and] run the risque of getting very inferior men'. He also agreed to
Telford's proposals for letting the earthwork in small lots to different persons, although he thought that 'the size of such lots
[ought] to be proportioned to the ability of the undertakers' in the
hope of finding some who 'may be able to manage a large contract,
or a number of small lots'.[37]

Simpson, Wilson and Cargill had all been employed on the Ellesmere Canal, undertaking the masonry contract on the Pontcysyllte
Aqueduct. Simpson had also been employed on virtually all of Telford's bridge contracts from 1790 onwards. The decision to bar
competition on the masonry contract was thus understandable,
given the wealth of experience offered by the successful contractors. Jessop's proposals over letting earth contracts in multiple
units appears to have become standard practice, only half a dozen
'firms' being involved in the main excavation work between 1804
and 1822. Records of contractors are not numerous, only the names
of Meak, Gillies, Ross, Davies and Hughes being recorded
amongst the general contractors.

Design changes

There were several changes in the design of canal features and line alterations. Telford examined the line of the canal in 1801 and again in 1802, using James Watt's survey as a guide.[38] The second survey was comparatively detailed, listing the number of locks, bridges, aqueducts and culverts. This plan was accepted by the Parliamentary Select Committee and was included in the application to Parliament for obtaining the initial grant of £20000.[39] In the Autumn of 1803 Telford was ordered to draw up a detailed plan of the canal suitable for reapplication to Parliament for a second more permanent Canal Act.[40] Jessop received instructions in late September to examine the line of canal.[41] In December 1803 he was ordered to prepare a report and estimate on the canal, using information supplied by Telford and his team of surveyors.[42] His report was submitted to the Board in February 1804, having first been endorsed by Telford.[43] It was then included in the papers used in obtaining the second Canal Act.[44]

The estimate of £474531 which was included in Jessop's report was considerably more than Telford's 1802 figure (£349617), mainly on account of the adoption of more expensive lock designs. The number of locks had been reduced by two to 23, and aqueducts reduced from twelve to seven, although bridges were up from twelve to 23.[45] As in other aspects of decision-making it is difficult to assess how much Jessop was influenced by Telford and his surveyors. Line changes had been decided upon before he even arrived in the Highlands, the position of the sea locks being altered after a joint report by Murdoch Downie and Mason.[46] General survey work proceeded well into 1804 and it was not until June of that year that Telford and Jessop received instructions to mark the exact position of the locks, bridges, weirs and culverts.[47] Many of the canal features were positioned during August 1804 although weirs and culverts were not definitely fixed, as their position depended on the raising of the fresh-water lochs, a task which was not to be performed until the completion of the project. Many of the weirs included on the original plans were not built until the 1840s.

The siting of locks and bridges in the middle district was also left open, as it was not intended to commence operations in that area until the two outer districts had been completed. Jessop was not involved in the detailed surveying of the middle district which did not start until the year of his departure in 1812.

Jessop appears to have been very much involved in the major design changes relating to lock construction and in the adoption of cast iron as a suitable material for bridge and lock gate construction. Telford had submitted turf-walled lock designs in his original 1801 survey. He argued that the slowness of operation would be counterbalanced by the cheapness of construction (at £5000/lock), and the accompanying estimate was based on the use of turf locks.[48] Jessop budgetted for more conventional masonry locks (at £7449 each) in his February 1804 estimate, which increased the overall cost of the project by £56 000. Telford, after considering the revised designs, gave his approval, though he stated he would not have accepted the revised plans if the cost for individual locks had exceeded £10 000. It is not known who was responsible for the design of the locks as built, although drawings of them are included in the Atlas of plates to Telford's 'Life'.[49]

Telford and Jessop decided to increase the size of the locks after a joint investigation into the type of vessel most likely to use the canal. They were assisted in this task by Sir William Rule, who supplied information on the size of Navy frigates and warships.[50] The decision to use cast iron for the lock gates appears to have been taken jointly, for Telford states in the 1814 Report that 'the high price of oak led Mr. Jessop and myself to adopt cast iron'.[51] The use of cast iron for accommodation bridges was also a joint decision, the basic design being based on swing bridges constructed in the West India Docks, a project which had strong Jessop connections.[52]

To conclude, Jessop's role in the project was essentially that of a monitor, rather than decision-maker. It was Telford who organized and carried out the initial survey work, it was Telford who recruited the managerial and contractual team and devised the procedure for their guidance and control, and it was Telford who handled all the problems of land purchase and finance. He was also responsible for the ordering and transportation of materials. Jessop was sent in by the Government to add weight to the project at a time when its future was uncertain; once the 1804 Canal Act had been obtained, his involvement in the project was limited to an annual joint inspection with Telford and to putting his signature to the latter's report to the Board of Commissioners. Telford continued to visit the construction site twice a year throughout the period of Jessop's association with the scheme, though this dropped to once a year after Jessop's departure.

Jessop's experience was undoubtedly a great help to Telford, who was, in comparison inexperienced in canal building, having been involved in the construction of only two canals (Ellesmere, as 'General agent' to Jessop, in 1793, and Shrewsbury in 1795) before his appointment as Engineer for the Caledonian in 1803. Jessop also had experience of inland lake and river navigation after work on the River Shannon. Apart from changing the design of locks and introducing cast iron, however, Jessop appears to have simply endorsed Telford's actions. He was also paid for his services, at least in the early years of the project, from Telford's own budget, which perhaps tells us much about his status vis-à-vis Telford and the canal.[53]

Resident and site engineers

It was through the next link in the managerial chain that Telford, and possibly Jessop, attempted to solve one of the major problems of the project – namely adequate control from a distance. An attempt is therefore made here to define the areas of responsibility allotted to the various site engineers and assistants with special regard to line and design changes and their overall contribution to the management and construction of the project.

As has already been noted, the evolution of the managerial structure was divided into two sections, the termination of survey work and the passing of the June 1804 Act marking the dividing point. Developments prior to June 1804 were concerned with controlling what was essentially a survey rather than a construction team. However, the basic procedure for the control of resident engineers engaged on construction work dates from this early period.

As previously stated, Telford had divided the project roughly in two, appointing Superintendents at each end, together with sundry assistants and surveyors. Provision was made for limited construction work in the two end basins which were marked out in the autumn of 1803. Fortunately, records of Telford's initial instructions to A. May, his Superintendent at Clachnaharry, have survived. They were written on 27 September, 1803, and ordered May to engage men for the excavation of Muirtown Basin and line of canal which extended from there to Clachnaharry. This line had been previously marked out by Telford and was to be excavated exactly to his directions. May was to ensure, if at all possible, that work was to 'be performed by the cubic yard, each man's work to be measured up monthly'.[54] Records of all expenditure were to be recorded in monthly paybills, which were to be dispatched, at regular intervals, to Telford, together with a journal of all that had occurred. Wages were to be fixed at 18*d* or 16*d*, according to quality of workmen.[55] Telford thus ensured full control over expenditure, accounts, type of labour to be used and line of canal to be excavated.

Similar instructions were sent to May's assistant, William Mackenzie, who was, when not engaged in recording the paybills, to visit the works and 'assist if necessary in measuring the work and in making agreements'.[56] A Mr Mason who was 'to manage the business about the quarries' appears to have had similar powers to May and Wilson, for Mackenzie was instructed 'to do the same with regard to Mr. Mason'.[57] John Wilson employed an assistant who dealt with the purchase and cutting of country timber.[58]

The early years of the project were thus very similar to other projects of the period, having a mixture of basic supervisory staff plus people allocated to one specific task, although on other projects this always appears to have been geared to the construction of one specific object or section, rather than to such matters as materials and finance, as appears to have been the case on the Caledonian. This degree of specialization does not appear to have been carried over into the post-1804 structure. During the months after September 1803, the individual members of the team were busily engaged on survey work, W. Hughes accompanying Jessop over the line at the end of October[58] and Mackenzie performing land valuations in the Corpach area.[59] The small number of workmen employed on excavation work was controlled by permanent overseers who presumably remained with the workmen on one particular site. The earliest reference to overseers is found in a Telford letter of February 1804.

'As well as engaging workmen and overseers it will be necessary to set them to work'.[60]

The essential elements of the managerial structure were therefore all present before the passing of the Canal Act in June 1804. The appointment of the two permanent Superintendents heralded the commencement of full-scale construction work. Telford was again responsible for drawing up their instructions, after receiving authorization from the Board for their appointment.[61] As before, the canal was divided up into two districts, each half having its own Superintendent, Mathew Davidson at Clachnaharry and John Telford at Corpach. No appointment was to be made for the middle district until the commencement of operations there.

Taken in conjunction with the earlier set of instructions, Telford's June 1804 directive provided the basic framework for the management of construction work up to the opening of the canal in 1822. As has been seen already, the superintendents were to let the cutting, puddling and embankments in small lots and 'where circumstances admit, a preference [was] to be given to letting several contracts to the same persons'.[62] They were also to let the masonry by contract. Telford was ordered by the Board to ensure that in 'no case whatever [was he] to allow the resident Superintendents upon the line of the canal to exceed the prices to be paid for labour, as previously settled by Mr. Jessop and himself, without specially reporting the same and receiving the sanction of the Board thereon'.[63] The Superintendents were also to ensure that the contractors kept in good repair any of the tools lent to them by the Commissioners. No mention was made of the recording of expenditure and procedure for the payment of workmen, which would suggest that they remained as before.

The instructions relating to the letting of masonry and general contracts appear to have been partially overruled by Telford and Jessop, as the line of canal and 'the mode in which the works are to be let' were decided in August 1804.[64] The Superintendents were allowed to fix rates 'applicable to particular places . . . according to the soil, situation and other circumstances,' subject to Telford's approval. In the event of the ground proving . . . .

'more difficult to work than the general appearance and trials already made had led us to conclude, a proportional allowance is to be made, but if any variation shall increase the expense above the rate of 6d. per yard on an average, every case of this kind is to be reported to Mr. Telford, and the agreement is only to be conditional until he has approved of the same.'[65]

As in the earlier 1803 instructions, Telford ensured rigid adherence to the prices fixed by him through the introduction of a clause giving him the right to reserve judgement on any increase. This feature was made more explicit in the June 1804 instructions.[66] Instances of increases in the contract prices were regularly recorded in Telford's annual reports, which would suggest that the above-mentioned safeguard worked efficiently.[67] Adherence to Telford's 'arrangements' by the Superintendents was given as one of the main reasons for the project's steady progress up to 1808.[68] No evidence exists to suggest that the Superintendents were not responsible for appointing general contractors. A very small number of individual firms was taken on, however, which would suggest that Telford and Jessop's desire that multiple units be let to single contractors was adhered to by Davidson and J. Telford.

On the occasions when design or line changes were implemented, as at Clachnaharry Sea Lock and Fort Augustus,[69] Telford and Jessop made all the major decisions, although much of the information must have been supplied by the Superintendents. Telford and Jessop also instructed the Superintendents as to where work should be concentrated, as in 1809 when they ordered Davidson to complete the section between Doughfour and Moulindour.[69] In addition to the 1804 provisions, the Superintendents played a vital role in the issue, transference and recording of finance and expenditure. From a comparatively early date, they were ordered to keep an exact record of all monies spent, in the form of a monthly pay-bill, which was sent to Telford together with all vouchers. It is also probable that the system of advanced monthly estimates introduced in 1804 was calculated by the Superintendents, as Telford made only two visits to the Highlands a year, although there is no documentary evidence for this assumption. The Superintendents received money direct from Telford rather than the Board.[70] It is not known if they handled all of the monthly allowance, although they did have control of the wages money, which was distributed by their subordinates. Since Telford was involved in all stages of ordering machinery it is conceivable that he paid the larger machinery and material suppliers directly from his account.

To conclude, it would appear that the Superintendents on the canal were kept in check by an elaborate system of monetary control and recording. Control of the money supply ensured control of contract price, wages and the amount of materials consumed. However, the Superintendents were responsible for the day–to–day running of the construction programme, receiving periodic visits from Telford and Jessop who decided any major issues on the spot. Their role in the managerial structure was thus second only to Telford. They do not appear to have had any say in what that role should be, the majority of decisions appertaining to this being taken before their appointment. The absence of detailed specifications for the project placed a greater emphasis on the skill and discretion of the Superintendents in carrying out Telford's wishes. Their very considerable achievement was marred by financial worries and inadequate supervision below Superintendent level, which resulted in structural failure and rebuilding in the 1840's.

Specialist staff

In addition to the permanent staff already mentioned, Telford employed specialists on particular topics, to advise on specific areas, usually relating to geographical features of the Highlands or machinery. In this first capacity, he employed Murdoch Downie, an Aberdeen sea captain, to survey the sea lochs and canal entrances, assisted by Mason.[71] Land valuation was carried out by George Brown of Elgin, probably the most experienced land valuer in the Highlands with A. Laughlands, another land surveyor and valuer, employed for the area around Fort William.[72] Numerous assistants and surveyors, including John Howell, and Barlow and Arrowsmith, were employed temporarily to carry out trial borings and to produce maps of the line of canal. Telford employed the Fyfe brothers to look after the pumping engines and at least one of the dredgers, and the Rhodes brothers of Hull on the design and construction of lock gates.[73] Bryan Donkin was consulted on an improved dredging machine.[74]

Lower management

Details of the lower managerial structure employed on the project are extremely scarce and vague, making it difficult to distinguish between those employed by the Commissioners and by the contractors. Immediately below the level of Superintendent came the post of General Assistant/Pay Clerk, which appears to have been occupied in the Clachnaharry district by Andrew May from 1804 to 1822.[74] He had previously been employed as temporary Superintendent before the appointment of Mathew Davidson. His main duties were the keeping of accounts and 'measuring the contents of the task work'.[75] The names of two other general assistants have been recorded, although their exact place of work is unknown. Presumably they were assigned to the western and middle districts. In pressing for a salary increase for the Assistants in 1813, Telford stated that they were paid £1.50 a week. He requested that this be increased to £100 per annum,[76] which gives some indication of the importance of the position.

The measurement of task or measure work, the main unit of labour on the canal, was a duty traditionally performed by assistant engineers, and it is not known if May and his colleagues worked on the actual line, measuring all the work as it was performed, or if they were based in site offices, receiving work records from overseers and possibly even Davidson and Easton. The large number of concurrent construction sites would tend to suggest that there were either more assistants/pay clerks whose existence was never recorded or, more probably, that it was the overseers who recorded the work performed on site. The small number of references to their being present on the construction site would suggest that they were concerned primarily with office work and that it was the overseers who controlled the project on the numerous construction sites. The number of overseers employed on the project varied from five to ten according to season, and was not affected by the number of workmen or sites.

May's knowledge of construction work was clearly very considerable, as he assumed the title of Superintendent for the Clachnaharry district after 1817.[77] It should be noted however that the main construction programme had moved to Fort Augustus by this period. It is not known if May continued in this capacity after the completion of the works at Fort Augustus. Reference is also made at this period to Clerk being employed at Fort Augustus as Superintendent.[78] Mathew Davidson had died earlier that year and had been replaced by his son, James, and Clerk's activities at Fort Augustus could possibly have been connected with these events.

The position of May and his colleagues was thus extremely ambiguous, appearing to require the qualities of engineer and accountant. There appears to have been considerable overlap between the roles of Superintendent, Assistant and Overseer, especially with regard to the measuring and recording of labour. There is even a remote possibility that the references to 'overseers and counters' recorded in the monthly employment figures, includes May and his colleagues, as no other record of their existence was kept, unless they were included under 'Mr. Telford's Clerks' in the annual management accounts.

The position of overseers in the managerial structure is also ambiguous. Overseers were included in the general employed figures, which recorded the number of carpenters, blacksmiths, masons and labourers. Presumably some of these workmen were hired directly by the Commissioners, but it would seem clear that the majority were technically employed by the contractors. Evidence of overseers coming within this second group is limited to isolated wage certificates and receipts. However, there is nothing to suggest that they were employed by the Commissioners. The names of at least two of the overseers are known, John Mackferson, Foreman of the Masons,[79] and Thomas Smith,[80] who had been employed by Telford prior to June 1804. The inclusion of overseers' signatures on all wage receipts would suggest that they kept records of work performed. It would also imply the formal handing over of money from one body to another.

The implications of this hypothesis are extremely serious as it would imply that the contractors had more agents on the construction site than the Commissioners and that the whole managerial team was dependent on co-operation between two groups whose interests sometimes conflicted, especially in the fields of finance and quality control. Detailed control of the project was left to the contractors (through their overseers), the Commissioners' agents providing overall supervision. There were possibly as few as five Government employees (the two Superintendents and three Assistants/Pay Clerks) on the project, if the above assumptions are correct. The duties of the overseers appear to correspond fairly closely to those of assistant engineers employed on contemporary civil engineering projects. They appear to have been responsible for one specific site, rather than large areas.

The importance of the contractors' overseers in the managerial structure would suggest that the contractors themselves played a key role. As has already been noted, the masonry contractors were well acquainted with Telford's working methods and the high standards demanded by him. Their permanent presence in the Highlands was virtually guaranteed by their heavy commitment to the Highland road and bridge scheme. They were provided with temporary accommodation at the commencement of the project but soon built themselves permanent dwellings at Inverness and later Fort Augustus.[81] One of them, John Wilson, had, as has already been noted, acted as Telford's temporary superintendent prior to June 1804. Telford appears to have been regularly accompanied by at least one of the masonry contractors on his annual tours of inspection. They were also involved in preparatory survey work, as can be seen from Telford and Wilson's investigation of Loch Oich in 1813.[82] They even acted as unofficial pay clerks, as Mathew Davidson reported in 1816:

> 'All is going well on the canal, I am in daily expectation of Mr. Telford here, Mr. Cargill and my son, James, are gone to pay the workmen at Fort Augustus.'[83]

To conclude, it would appear that the mysterious lack of information regarding Government supervisory staff under the level of assistant/pay clerk was due to the fact that there were none. The rest of the managerial team was made up of the contractors and their overseers. As a result, the contractors enjoyed a very considerable amount of freedom which resulted in shoddy workmanship and transgression from what was required. The problems were most apparent in the western and middle divisions, which contained a large proportion of the masonry works. Banavie Locks especially were not provided with adequate foundations or side walls, which resulted in rapid deterioration.[84]

It will never be known if Telford and his assistants were aware of these shortcomings at the time. May in his 1837 report certainly suggests that there was deliberate concealment:

> 'I have reason to believe that the contractor for these locks, while engaged in the actual execution of the works, was fully under the conviction (which was shared by many others at the time) that the navigation was a thing which was never to take effect and that his locks would consequently never require to come into actual operation'.
> '. . . That so imperfect a description of workmanship should have satisfied, or rather escaped the severe reprehension of Mr. Telford on his oc-

casional visitations to the canal, is surprising, and can only be accounted for on the supposition, which I believe to be a correct one, that the utmost pains were taken by the contractor to conceal, by a variety of arts, the true nature of his proceedings.'

Had the managerial structure been balanced in favour of the Commissioners rather than the contractors, shortcomings would have been corrected. In a time of high inflation the trust and freedom given to the contractors counted for nothing, and ironically, the rigid system of price control forced them into taking the obvious way out, namely bad workmanship. The problems of supervising so extensive a site, lack of capital, and eventually possibly lack of faith in the project all contributed to the further and continuing delays, so that by the time the Caledonian Canal had been completed it had been overtaken by events, and never fulfilled the hopes of those who had initiated the project.

Bibliography

Cameron A.D. *The Caledonian Canal*. Lavenham 1972, Terence Dalton Ltd.

Haldane A. R. B. *New ways through the Glens*. London, Thomas Nelson, 1962

Hadfield C. and Skempton A. W. *William Jessop*. Newton Abbot, David & Charles, 1979.

Rolt L. T. C. *Thomas Telford*, Longmans Green & Co., London, 1958

References

1. Third Report from the Committee on the Survey of the Coasts, etc. of Scotland. Caledonian Canal. June, 1803. Appendix 4.
2. *Ibid.*
3. 1st Caledonian Canal Report, 1804. (referred to subsequently as '1st Report').
4. Minutes of 2nd Caledonian Canal Meeting, 4 Aug., 1803.
5. Minutes of 11th Caledonian Canal Meeting, 6 Feb., 1804.
6. 1st Report 3. Accounts (Management) and Telford's instructions to May and Mackenzie, 27 September 1803.
7. Jessop to Rickman, 29 September, 1803. Jessop was Mayor of Newark at the time of Telford's departure for the Highlands in August 1803, and was unable to attend any canal business until October, requesting that instructions be sent direct to him.
8. Telford to Cameron of Lochiel, 3 October 1803. Scottish Record Office (SRO), MT1/1.

9. 1st Report, Appendix F. 'Report on the intended entrance from the Western Sea, at Corpach on Loch Eil by Messrs Downie and Mason, Fort William, 2 September 1803'.

10. *Ibid.*, Management and Survey Accounts.

11. 2nd Caledonian Canal Report, 1805 (referred to subsequently as '2nd Report').

12. Minutes of 19th Caledonian Canal Meeting, 11 June 1804; 2nd Report, Appendix C.

13. Telford to Jessop, 8 June, 1804.

14. See Rolt L. T. C. *Thomas Telford*. London, Longmans Green and Co., 1958, for general details of association between Jessop, Davidson and Telford.

15. *Ibid.* John Telford appears to have acted as Telford's personal draughtsman, preparing plans for Bridgnorth Church in the 1790s.

16. Telford to Jessop, 8 June, 1804.

17. *Ibid.* This proposal does not appear to have been implemented, Mathew Davidson assuming responsibility for the centre district.

18. 2nd Report, Appendix D; Jessop to Telford, 9 June, 1804.

19. *Ibid.*, Accounts (Management).

20. Jessop to Telford, 9 June, 1804.

21. 2nd Report.

22. 4th Caledonian Report, 1807; Also, Cameron, A. D. *The Caledonian Canal*. Laverham, Terence Dalton, Ltd., 1972, p.67.

23. Telford to Jessop, 8 June, 1804.

24. *Ibid.*

25. Telford to A. May, 27 Sept., 1803. SRO, MT1/1.

26. 2nd Report.

27. Telford to Rickman, 6 June, 1804. SRO MT1/1.

28. 2nd Report, Appendix C; Telford to Jessop, 8 June, 1804.

29. *Ibid.*, Main Report.

30. *Ibid.*, Appendix K. Report of Telford and Jessop, autumn 1804.

31. Telford to Cameron of Lochiel, 2 Sept. 1803, SRO MT1/1.

32. 2nd Report, Appendix B.

33. *Ibid.*, Main report and Machinery Accounts.

34. Skempton A. W. A history of the steam dredger, 1793–1830. *Trans. Newcomen Soc.*, 1974, 47, 103.

35. Donkin, S. B. Bryan Donkin, FRS, MICE, 1768–1855. *Trans. Newcomen Soc.*, 1949–51, 27,

36. Telford to Jessop, 8 June, 1804.

37. Jessop to Telford, 9 June, 1804.

38. *Op. cit.*, ref. 1, Appendix I.

39. *Ibid*, Main report.

40. 1st Report 'Instructions to Mr Telford'.
41. *Ibid.*, Main report.
42. Minutes of 7th Caledonian Canal Meeting, 25 Nov. 1803.
43. 1st Report, and minutes of 11th Caledonian Canal Meeting.
44. Telford to Rickman, 15 Febr., 1804. SRO MT1/1.
45. 1st Report Jessop's report and estimate.
46. *Ibid.* See also refs. 7 and 9.
47. 2nd Report, Main report.
48. *Op. cit.* ref. 1, Appendix 1, Telford's 1801 report.
49. Rickman J. *Life of Thomas Telford*. London, 1838. *Atlas* Plate.
50. 2nd Report, Main report. Jessop's knowledge of Baltic shipping was non-existent, as he had told the June 1803 Select Committee.
51. 11th Caledonian Canal Report, 1814, Appendix C.
52. 3rd Caledonian Canal Report, 1806. It had originally been intended to construct timber bridges, similar to those on the Fortth and Clyde, but after consultations with Jessop, Telford decided to use cast iron.
53. Telford to Rickman, 24 March, 1804. SRO MT1/1.
54. A. May, 27 Sept., 1803. SRO MT1/1.
55. *Ibid.* The wage rates were listed only for day work.
56. Telford to W. Mackenzie, 27 Sept., 1803. SRO MT1/1.
57. *Ibid.* Reference was made in the 1805 accounts to Mackenzie as 'Superintendent' for the Clachnaharry district, although Telford's 1803 instructions make it clear that it was May who was given more responsibility. Mackenzie received £145 up to September 1804, including fees for land valuation.
58. Telford to Rickman, 31 Oct., 1803. SRO MT1/1.
59. Telford to Cameron of Lochiel, 22 Dec., 1803. SRO MT1/1.
60. Telford to Rickman, 18 Feb., 1804. SRO MT1/1.
61. Minutes of 19th Caledonian Canal Meeting, 11 June, 1804.
62. Jessop to Telford, 9 June, 1804.
63. 2nd Report, Appendix E.
64. *Ibid*, Main report.
65. *Ibid*, Appendix M. Prices of labour and workmanship, as determined by Messrs Jessop and Telford.
66. See Telford to Jessop, 8 June 1804, where constant reference is made to 'subject to my determination' and 'to be determined by you or myself' with regard to fixing of prices.
67. Telford and Jessop agreed to price changes in the contract for masonry in October 1806 (4th Caledonian Canal Report, 1807) and general excavation work performed by Meek in 1813 (11th Caledonian Canal Report, 1814).
68. 6th Caledonian Canal Report, 1809.

69. *Ibid.* 'Considerable' design changes were made at Clachnaharry sea lock during Telford and Jessop's 1807 autumn visit: the proposed coffer dam was scrapped and replaced by a solid embankment out of which the lock pit was to be eventually excavated.

70. *Ibid.* Money was paid into Telford's special bank account and then drawn out to pay for construction work: Presumably the Superintendants had some arrangement whereby they could draw money from this account in Telford's absence.

71. 1st Report.

72. 2nd Report.

73. Mitchell J. *Reminiscences of my life in the Highlands.* Vol. 1, 68.

74. 14th Caledonian Canal Report, 1817, Appendix E.

75. May was also responsible for handling early steamship business on the canal. See Haldane, A. R. B. *New ways through the glen.* London, Thomas Nelson, 1962.

76. Minutes of 63rd Caledonian Canal Meeting, 1813.

77. Paybill, Sept.–Oct., 1819. House of Lords Record Office (HLRO).

78. *Ibid.* Clerk received £7. 15s. 10d. a month, as did May at Clachnaharry.

79. Wage certificates, 1807–8. HLRO.

81. Cameron, *op.cit.*, ref. 22, p.55. Simpson and Cargill built houses in Telford Street, Inverness. Southey refers to Cargill having built himself a stone house at Fort Augustus.

82. *Ibid.*, p.78

83. Mathew Davidson to Hope, 12 Sept., 1816. HLRO.

84. Cameron, *op.cit.* ref.22, p.130. May had pointed out that the masonry in the Banavie flight was particularly bad.

8

Telford's highland bridges

JOHN R. HUME

Thomas Telford's association with bridge-building in the high-lands of Scotland stemmed from a growing awareness of the econ-omic value of roads. From the middle of the 18th century, systematic road improvement in southern central and eastern Scot-land had gone hand in hand with agricultural reform and industrial growth. In part road and bridge building had been accomplished by turnpike trusts,[1] but to a greater linear extent by the county authorities, using money provided by commutation of statute labour.[2] The few mediaeval and early modern bridges over major rivers[3] were to a growing extent complemented by new and improved bridges, many designed after the French pattern, offer-ing less obstruction to floodwater, and at the same time, with wider carriageways and on flatter curves, aiding the development of wheeled traffic.[4] The first Scottish coach services appear to have been started in the 1740s, and by the end of the century internal road communication within lowland Scotland, and between Scot-land and England was well established.[5] With coastal and river navigations, canals, and wagonways,[6] one could say that central Scotland was at that time as well served as any part of the UK.

Matters were somewhat different in the highlands. The physical barriers to communication imposed by mountainous terrain, by a deeply indented coastline, by bogs, major rivers, and minor streams liable to sudden and violent flooding could only be over-come in cases of extreme military or economic necessity. The trade in black cattle with the lowlands, and, ultimately, with England, was served by seasonal droving over well-established routes which were, in the highlands, not confined to roads.[7] After the abortive Jacobite risings of 1715 and 1745, both mounted from within the highlands, military considerations led to the construction of a fairly extensive network of roads with many minor and a few major bridges, designed principally to serve a chain of three forts, Fort George, Fort Augustus and Fort William, with a group of less heavily fortified barracks. These roads were built by troops as a summer exercise, and were designed for rapid movement of foot soldiers on routes of military rather than economic significance. As the threat of armed rising receded the network was to some extent allowed to fall into decay, but some routes, such as that through the Great Glen, and most of the major bridges were adopted by the highlanders as civil communication routes.[8]

There were four important reasons why pressure for the extension and improvement of road communications within the highlands built up from the 1780s. One was the growing divergence between living conditions in the highlands and the lowlands. More efficient agriculture and industrial development brought higher wages, superior housing and a better and more varied diet to the lowlander. The improved communications already alluded to make him more mobile. Both highland landowner and highland tenant became aware of the difference: the landowner sought to improve his land and to introduce industry in order to increase his income and, dare it be said, to ameliorate the lot of his tenantry; the tenant hoped to better his condition by enlistment in the army, by migration, or by engaging in the landlord's new schemes. The aspirations of both, it was hoped, could be met by the introduction of 'productive industry', by the development of fishing and by agrarian change. All these involved, of necessity, improvement of internal communication and of links with the lowlands. These 'internal' needs were, in the 1790s and early 1800s, reinforced by the desire of the UK government to maintain population in the highlands as a source of revenue, and as a recruiting ground for both the army and the navy.[9]

Initial impetus

The initial stimulus to the construction and improvement of roads in the highlands seems to have been channelled through two influential bodies: the British Fisheries Society[10] founded in 1784,[11] and the Highland Society of Scotland. The former did, indeed, from 1786 develop a series of fishing stations on both the east and the west coasts of the mainland and in the Inner and Outer

Hebrides. Although these were all mainly served by sea, their existence added to the demand for internal transport, and the society did
in fact build a road from Contin to Ullapool.[12] The Highland
Society, largely composed of landowners, was more of a pressure
group, though an influential one.

The question one might ask, in the light of the evident desirability of road and bridge construction in the highlands, is why the
highland landowners did not, either individually or collectively,
invest in road building themselves? The answer lies fundamentally
in the relative poverty of the region, the large expanses of uncultiv-
able, and hence non-traffic-generating land, the height of the
passes, and, perhaps most important, the physical difficulties of
road building in country where native rock is always near the surface, where water courses abound, and where flash floods are
common and devastating. Had it been left to the highland proprietors alone, no doubt gradual extension of the network would have
proceeded, but national, and indeed extra-national considerations
galvanized the state into an unprecedented involvement in the *civil*
affairs of Scotland. As Telford put it in his report:

> 'The Empire at large being deeply interested in those Improvements, as
> it regards promoting the Fisheries, and increasing the Revenue and
> Population of the Kingdom, justifies government in granting Aid
> towards making Roads and Bridges in a Country which must other-
> wise remain, perhaps for Ages to come, thus imperfectly connected'.[13]

'Unprecedented involvement' is a bold phrase to use. It can
indeed only justifiably be employed with reference to the extent of
government assistance. There were certainly precedents in kind.
The county Commissioners for Supply for Aberdeenshire, Argyllshire and Perthshire received grants in aid of bridge building from
the 1770s,[14] and state money was also loaned for the completion of
the Forth and Clyde and Crinan canals.[15] The government also assisted from time to time the improvement of strategic harbours,
such as that at Peterhead.[16] The largest of these commitments was
the £50 000 loaned to the Company of Proprietors of the Forth and
Clyde Canal in 1784. Even allowing for war-time inflation this is
small beer in comparison with the £252 000 capital grant given by
the state towards the construction of the road and bridge network.[17] To this must be added a continuing commitment to main-

tain not only grant-aided roads and bridges but also selected lengths of military and other roads.[18] Far overshadowing this was the money made available for the construction of the Caledonian Canal, wholly funded by government as a strategic link, but also creating work in the highlands and designed to aid the fishing industry. By the time it was sufficiently complete to allow sea-to-sea passage, the canal had cost the taxpayer nearly £1 million.[19]

The government's thinking on Highland communications was crystallized in Thomas Telford's two 'Surveys and reports on the Coasts and Central Highlands of Scotland' made by command of the Lords Commissioners of the Treasury in 1801 and 1802.[20] His second and final report was published in three sections, dealing with 'What regards rendering the Intercourse of the Country more perfect, by means of Bridges and Roads'; the Caledonian Canal; and Naval Stations and Fisheries. Telford undertook two extensive tours to familiarize himself with the physical and human problems, but also sought the advice of the Highland Society of Scotland, which formed a subcommittee of its directors to prepare its own statement, printed as an appendix to the first part of Telford's 1802 report.[21]

Their joint proposals were for a network of roads based on trunk routes to the north up the east coast, and to the west at Arisaig, together with subsidiary roads linked with these, and for providing internal links on the islands of Skye, Jura, Islay and Mull (Fig. 1). Ferries, with the necessary piers were also projected for inter-island, sea-loch and some major river crossings, but the proposals also included the construction of four bridges to replace ferry crossings on the rivers Tay, Spey, Beauly and Conon. The Highland Society also requested bridges over the Dornoch Firth and Loch Fleet. Telford estimated that the cost of his proposals (four major bridges and nearly 1000 miles of road) would be £62 000, and stated that 'if they were undertaken by proper persons they might be executed in three years'.[22] The Highland Society's report, stressing the importance of roads and bridges, especially for fishing, pressed for a government grant, and suggested the appointment of a commission to supervise the work.

The report was immediately considered by a select committee of the House of Commons, which recommended in June 1803 that grant aid should be made available for road and bridge construc-

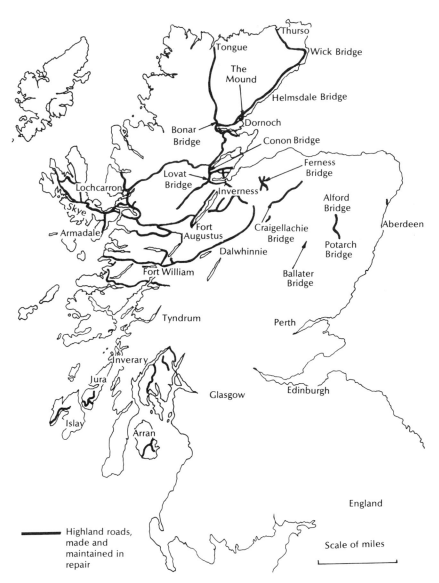

Fig. 1. Telford's roads in Scotland

tion.[23] By the end of July an Act of Parliament had been passed (43 George III cap. 80) authorizing such assistance, and setting up a commission to control the expenditure of the money. The chairman was Charles Abbot, Speaker of the House of Commons, and the other members included Nicholas Vansittart, Chancellor of the Exchequer, and other directors of the British Fisheries Society. Clearly the government attached great weight to the proposals. The basic argument in favour was stated by the select committee:

> 'they have not recommended that the smallest additional burden be thrown on the public unless to prevent that emigration which will deprive the country of its hardiest and bravest protectors who have distinguished themselves most conspicuously by sea and land, and with a view to improve that commerce which must amply repay the pecuniary assistance your Committee have thought it their duty to advise'.[24]

Design problems

Telford's approach to the problem of designing and constructing the hundreds of bridges required for the highland road system was initially conservative. He had considerable experience of masonry construction which he applied to the larger bridges, such as Dunkeld, which were made of cut sandstone. Most of the smaller bridges were made of rubble, as far as possible from sedimentary or metamorphic rocks, though local igneous or intrusive rocks were used for spandrels and wing walls. Only in the largest bridges was there any real sophistication of design; elsewhere Telford was concerned with the most economical approach consonant with durability. He was very careful of his choice of sites, combining his usual eye for a good line of road with consideration of the needs of the country, and of geologically suitable locations. For example, he reported of Dunkeld:

> 'the best situation for a bridge is a little way above the lower ferry; at this place there is a strait reach of the river and in winter the ice is broke by passing over a ford nearly opposite the mouth of the river Braan. This situation will also connect with the improved lines of road which are proposed to be made on each side of the river'.[25]

At Fochabers he chose a point 'Where a rock passes about eight to ten feet below ordinary low water, precisely in the line of the present road'.[26]

Apart from the financial and accounting problems encountered by the Commissioners, which are outside the scope of this paper, there were difficulties in securing contractors who would complete work on time and to acceptable standards. Extreme examples of ineptitude were Lochgoilhead Bridge on the Ardnoe Road 'which from unskilfulness and disagreement among the workmen has fallen down no less than four times'[27] and Borlam Bridge which was 'accidentally destroyed' in 1808.[28] Far more serious than any human inadequacy, however, was the highland weather. The tendency of the highland rivers to sudden and serious floods, often bringing down trees and other debris, was well known to Telford and his contractors, who consulted local informants where possible,[29] but there was no reliable hydrological information, and the estimation of clear waterways was correspondingly approximate. In places where earlier bridges had been swept away as at Nethy Bridge and Ballater the inadequate designs were a gauge, but elsewhere Telford noted:

'In highland rivers, where in general the stream has not before been noticed with any correctness, it is only by degrees that the proper dimensions of bridges can be ascertained: that is in rainy seasons only, and by continuing the observations through a succession of these seasons. The bridges now built will serve for a scale of measurement, each for its own river; and we have already found that the water-way which at the time of building was supposed to be unnecessarily ample has experimentally proved too small. A striking instance of this has occurred in the last bridge built by Messrs. Simpson and Wilson, near the termination of the Lochy-side road at Loch Arkaig, the intended arch was considered extravagantly large by Mr Wilson himself, but he happened to possess centring rather larger than the specification, and did not choose to lessen it. This bridge in October 1811 was nearly filled by the swollen river, part of one of the abutments was undermined, and the arch so much shattered that contractors have been forced to take it down and rebuild it.'[30]

A bridge over the River Spean on the Laggan road, also swept away in the October 1811 floods, had its waterway increased from 80 to 90 ft in the rebuild, but in October 1812 one pier was swept away. In consequence the waterway was enlarged to 100 ft and the bridge raised by 3 ft.[31]

The destructive force of floods was much increased by floating timber. In the 1812 floods the centering for the Potarch Bridge was badly damaged by single logs being floated down to Aberdeen by timber contractors.[32] This vulnerability to damage was one of the reasons for the substitution of cast iron for masonry at Bonar and Craigellachie. Bonar was in fact assailed by floating timber 'with such violence that the crash of the timber was heard at a considerable distance' but was unaffected.[33] The disastrous floods of August 1829, which destroyed the bridges at Fochabers, Ballater and Carr and badly damaged many other masonry bridges, left Craigellachie relatively unharmed.[34] Given the degree of uncertainty involved it is surprising that so many of Telford's highland bridges survive in virtually original condition.

The bridges

The bridges themselves fall organizationally into four categories: strategic bridges envisaged in the original report; other major bridges executed as separate contracts; bridges built as part of road contracts; and bridges designed as replacements for flood-damaged structures.

The four strategic bridges. In his 1803 report Telford commented that 'in those parts where they [the military roads] are tolerably accessible, or where roads have since been formed by the inhabitants, the use of them is very much circumscribed from the want of bridges over some of the principal rivers'. He specifically mentioned bridges over the Tay at Dunkeld, over the Spey at Fochabers, over the Beauly and over the Conon near Dingwall which 'are all crossed by means of ferry boats' where 'accidents frequently happen'.[35]

Dunkeld Bridge was stated to be 'of the first importance to the central highlands; it would accommodate a great district of that country, and at the same time facilitate the communication with the north highlands.' The landowner, the Duke of Atholl, owner of the ferry at Dunkeld, was willing to put up half the expense in exchange for a toll to be used to liquidate the debt. The difficulty in securing materials that affected Telford in many places is here made explicit. He reported that 'it is probable that a flat rubble stone will be got near the slate quarries, which are within a short distance of the place'. 'Freestone of durable quality', on the other hand had to be brought by water to Perth, and thence by land. The estimated cost was £15 000.[36] Despite subsequent widening of the carriage-way and deepening of the foundations, the work, completed in 1808, was executed for only £13 360 19s 6d.[37] The ornamental character of the work (Figs 2 and 3) and the use of hollow abutments and spandrels distinguish the bridge from most of the other highland structures. So far as one can judge, there were more problems in obtaining the Duke of Atholl's formal commitment to the project than in its construction. It is the only one of the four strategic bridges still substantially in original condition.

The Spey Bridge was designed to replace a 'very dangerous ferry', over a river 'rapid and deep, being the drain of a great extent of mountainous country, where there is much rain'. Though the Spey is essentially a highland river, this bridge served primarily a lowland function, being 'on the great coast road eastward from Inverness and Fort George through the towns and cultivated country in Moray and Banffshire from whence it passes through Fraserburgh and Peterhead to Aberdeen.' A subscription was raised by the Duke of Gordon, who sought government assistance to complete the bridge: this was given in the form of a special grant, and the bridge was completed in 1806.[38] After the floods of 1829, which washed out two spans, a single laminated wooden arch was installed.[39] When this became life-expired in 1853 a cast-iron arch was substituted, and this, strengthened in steel, still survives, though the bridge no longer carries road traffic.[40]

The bridges over the Beauly and Conon were 'greatly wanted in order to facilitate the communications with Ross-shire, Sutherland and Caithness; they are equally so for the north west coast of the mainland and the northern parts of the Hebrides; they are the roots from which a great number of branches of roads are to proceed, which are necessary for the improvement of the country, and the extension of the fisheries'. Telford estimated that they would cost £5000 each.[41] Conon was a straightforward masonry structure. Delay in securing a county assessment act for Ross and Cromarty postponed construction, but it was contracted for in 1807 and the bridge was completed in 1809.[42]

The Beauly crossing presented more problems. Telford's original scheme was for a 'wooden bridge of American Pitch Pine', but the Commissioners were unhappy about the commitment of public money to a temporary structure, unless a repair fund could

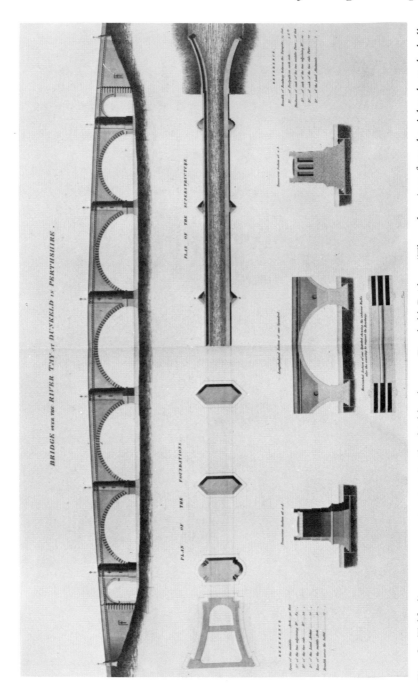

Fig. 2. Telford's masonry masterpiece in the highlands was Dunkeld Bridge. (These drawings from the Atlas show the hollow spandrels and abutments which he had introduced in 1805 at Tongland)

Fig. 3. Dunkeld Bridge today, from the NE

be accumulated.[43] It was, as planned, the longest of the highland bridges, with a 470 ft waterway, its nearest rival being Dunkeld with 446 ft. In 1809 an improved ferry (probably of the chain type) was being considered.[44] It was not until 1811 that an Act was passed (50 Geo III c 87) providing for the maintenance of the bridge, and a 5-span masonry structure to be known as Lovat Bridge was commissioned. Construction of foundations proved difficult,[45] but the bridge was completed in October 1814, when a toll was levied to provide for repairs.[46] This bridge still carries main road traffic, although the gradients have been eased by building up the spandrels. Conon Bridge was demolished in the 1960s after it had proved inadequate to handle heavy loads for the construction of Dounreay Power Station.

Other major crossings. In the Highland Society's comments appended to Telford's 1803 report[47] two further major crossings were proposed, over the Dornoch Firth at Invershin, and over the Fleet. These would, with Telford's major bridges, open up a ferry-free route to the extreme north, and most significantly, to the important fishing station at Wick. The Society claimed that at Invershin 'a bridge can easily be thrown over'. In practice it proved more difficult. The stimulus to construction was probably a terrible ferry disaster in 1809, witnessed by John Mitchell, Telford's General Superintendent of Highland Roads, in which more than 100 people were drowned.[48] As on the Beauly, an improved ferry was proposed. This was definitely of the chain type, modelled on the Renfrew Ferry on the Clyde.[49] By 1811, however, the manner of the crossing, and its place had been settled. The choice was between Criech and Bonar:

> 'In this dilemma Mr Telford felt himself justified by the measurements which had been taken at Bonar Ferry to propose an iron bridge at that place . . . A plan of an iron bridge of one arch spanning one hundred and fifty feet was hereupon prepared and having recently obtained the approbation of the County of Sutherland will be proceeded in without delay'.[50]

The design (Fig. 4) was a reduced version of the 500 ft span proposed for the Menai Straits crossing in 1810.[51] Problems were encountered in establishing the foundations of the south abutment and two masonry arches, one 60 ft and one 50 ft, were substitu-

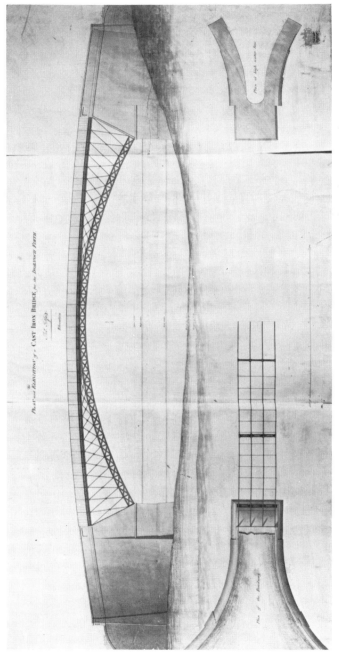

Fig. 4. Bonar Bridge as designed (Telford Mss, Institution of Civil Engineers).

ted.[52] The contractors, Simpson and Cargill made use of coffer dams and caissons in sinking the piers through 8 ft of gravel. Telford's employment of such experienced men shows his intent to make a success of a novel design.

> 'The iron-work was cast at the Foundry of Mr. Hazledine at Pontcysyllte in Denbeighshire, where for the greater certainty the arch itself was fitted together on temporary abutments and scaffolding in June last [1812] and when found perfect in every particular, was taken to pieces, carried by canal conveyance to Chester, and shipped for the Dornoch Firth where it all arrived safe in the beginning of September; and the centering of the arch being already fixed and fitted for its reception, the iron-castings were speedily reconstructed in their proper form, after which the upper part of the masonry, the road-way, and iron railing was finished, and the whole bridge being completed in all its parts was finally inspected and approved in the beginning of November last' – one year early.[53]

Telford introduced at least two innovations in this bridge, according to his own account. The Commissioners commented that 'the roadway is supported by bearers of a lozenge form, which combine the advantages of internal strength with external appearance'.[54] Telford compared these to the supports of a cast-iron aqueduct erected on the Shrewsbury Canal in 1796 – presumably Longdon on Tern. The cross-joint pieces were modelled on those used at Pontcysyllte Aqueduct on the Ellesmere Canal, completed in 1805. The innovations were in the design of the ribs, of which there were four, each cast in five pieces. The sections were 30 ft × 3 ft × 2½ in. thick. They were pierced by triangular openings, leaving all the solid parts 6 in. in breadth. Telford commented 'this sameness of dimension is of importance in the practice of casting iron as the whole thereby cools equally. It is here introduced for the first time.' Telford also believed that the fastening of the arch to the abutments, used here, was also new.[55] Bonar Bridge proved very successful, resisting attack by ice and tree trunks, and by a sloop (in August 1826) which drifted into the bridge: the mast was snapped off 2 ft above the deck, but the bridge was undamaged.[56] It was eventually destroyed in a flood about 1892, not however through any defect in the ironwork.[57]

The crossing of the Fleet 'by a bridge' suggested by the Highland Society also proved more complicated than anticipated. In its mature version of 1812, Telford's plan was for a protective embankment almost 1000 yards long, with a bridge at the north end fitted with non-return flap valves to prevent the incoming tide flowing beyond the embankment. It was reckoned that this would defend about 100 acres of already cultivated land from the sea, and would allow a further 400 acres to be reclaimed. The value of this to the landowner, the Marquis of Stafford, was agreed at £1000, and the residual cost of £7400 was accepted for grant aid by the Commissioners.[58] The volume of earthwork was considerable: the mound was 60 ft wide at the base and 23 ft high. The bridge, of four arches, was completed in 1815, together with a temporary wooden crossing of the breach, which was closed at the second attempt on 18 June, 1816.[59] Two sluice arches were added in 1834, on the recommendation of Joseph Mitchell, at a cost of £532.[60] With its completion (Fig. 5) communication was 'perfected to the remotest part of Scotland without the necessity of submitting to the inconvenience of a single ferry'.[61]

With the exception of Fochabers Bridge, all the structures described so far were part of the grand road to the north. The Commissioners viewed this as a prime element in their strategy, and stressed the significance of the bridges themselves: 'The erection of bridges over unfordable rivers is a measure of more urgent importance than even the formation of carriage roads in the highlands'[62] and valued the completed structures accordingly: 'the bridges of Dunkeld, Lovat, Conan and Bonar [form] a connected series of bridges which for size, solidity and utility is not surpassed anywhere in the Kingdom'.[63] The other major bridges executed in this series were Wick, sought by the British Fisheries Society to replace a shaky wooden structure[64] and completed as early as June 1807,[65] and Helmsdale (Fig. 6), not a bridge of unusual size but undertaken under a separate contract. The Commissioners noted:

'we have hitherto found that bridges undertaken distinctly from roads have proceeded without the irregularities which we have been compelled to notice in several of the road-contractors; the expenses of bridge-building being more easily reducible to a certainty, and the masons who undertake large bridges being generally men of experience in these matters.'[66]

Helmsdale was completed in 1811. Wick was replaced in 1877,

Fig. 5. The Mound, from the North, showing the flap sluices with their control house and the massive embankment beyond

the outline of the original bridge being preserved: Helmsdale still stands, though now bypassed for main road traffic.

The other large bridges financed as separate contracts by the Commissioners (Table 1) were built in response to 'memorials' drawn up by local people, and though linked with existing or projected roads, were intended primarily to solve purely local problems. Wick really falls into this class, although it later formed part of the great road to the north.

Four other masonry bridges were built, of which the largest was Ballater. A crossing of the Dee at Ballater was of great consequence to the local inhabitants, as there were no bridges nearer than Braemar and Aberdeen. A bridge had been built in 1783 at a cost of £1700, but it was swept away in 1799. To replace it a subscription was raised to which not only the landowners but also, and most unusually, the tenants contributed.[67] The bridge was built in 1808–09, and was completed 'in the firmest manner'.[68] It was one of the casualties of the great floods of August 1829, having survived bombardment by floating logs on a number of occasions.[69] After the completion of Ballater, a second bridge over the Dee was requested, and a site chosen by Telford in August 1810 at Potarch, near Kincardine O'Neil. Attempts had previously been made to build a bridge at this site, where there is a ridge of rock across the river.[70] Construction of the bridge was well under way in October 1812

Table 1. Bridges built by distinct contracts★

Bridge	No. of arches	Spans, ft	Dates of construction	Cost, £
Alford	3	40+40+40	1811	2000
★ Ballater	5	34+55+60+55+34	1808–09	3904
Bonar	3	50+60+150	1814	13 971
Conon	5	45+55+65+55+45	1807–09	6854
Craigcllachie	4	150+15+15+15	1814	8200
Dunkeld	7	20+74+84+90+84+74+20	1806–09	13 361
Ferness	3	36+55+36	1815	1255
Helmsdale	2	70+70	1809–11	
Lovat	5	40+50+60+50+40	1812–14	8802
Potarch	3	65+70+65	1811–13	4067
Wick	3	48+60+48	1805–07	2000

★ Sources: Rickman, *op cit.*, 170; 8th Report of Commissioners, BPP, 1817, 9, 28; dates from Reports of Commissioners, *passim.*

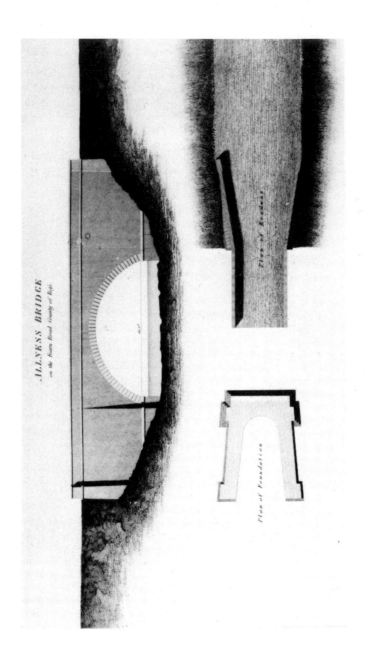

ALLNESS BRIDGE
on the Town Road County of Ross

Plan of Foundation

Plan of Recess

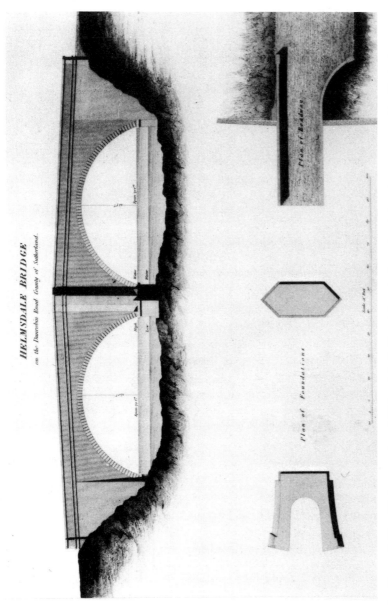

Fig. 6. Alness Bridge (facing page) and Helmsdale Bridge (above), from the Atlas showing two of Telford's less spectacular bridges

Fig. 7. Ferness Bridge, very typical of Telford's smaller 3-span bridges

when it was hit by timber being floated down river.[71] The bridge
was, however duly completed in October 1813,[72] and still stands.

The building of Potarch opened up a new route into northern
Aberdeenshire and Banffshire, and this was extended by the construction of Bridge of Alford, on the petition of one local landowner, a Mr Farquharson of Haughton, who also contracted for
the work. This was finished in November 1811.[73] Very similar to
Alford in conception and design was Ferness (Fig. 7), proposed in
1813[74] and completed in 1815[75]. This bridge was badly damaged in
the 1829 floods,[76] but like Alford survives as a bridge carrying traffic.

The last of this group of bridges is also the most important technically, though not necessarily economically. Craigellachie Bridge
was built after a memorial in 1811 in favour of a crossing at Boat of
Bridge had been rejected as being too near Fochabers.[77] Telford
proposed instead an iron bridge at Craigellachie, at an estimated
cost of £8000, noting that 'no stone bridge could be built unless at
an immoderate expense.'[78] The span was to be a replica of that
already designed for Bonar, and the lower cost in part reflects the
existence of a precedent. The account of its construction illustrates
an important aspect of the value of cast iron for highland bridge
construction. The ironwork was cast by Hazledine at Plas

Fig. 8. Craigellachie Bridge as it was in 1973, showing its superb lines

Kynaston, Pontcysyllte, and was delivered by sea to the Moray Firth coast in July 1814. August and September sufficed for the fitting and fixing of the ironwork, and the delay in opening until November 1814 was due to the time taken to widen the north approach road, which had to be cut through solid rock.[79] The bridge resisted the effects of the floods of 1829, though the short approach spans were washed out.[80] It had some parts replaced in steel in 1965, and is now bypassed (Fig. 8).

Bridges built as part of road contracts. These were naturally the most numerous of the highland bridges. According to Rickman[81] most of them were under 10 ft in span. There was a degree of standardization of design in that bridges of 40–50 ft span were built to specifications drawn up by Telford at the beginning of the programme in 1803.[82] Details are given in Table 2.

Table 2

Types of bridge	Number	Waterway
One arch	1075	10 198
Two arches	13	643
Three arches	16	1236
Five arches	2	222
Total	1106	12 299

Some of the 2 and 3 arch bridges are of considerable size. Contin, for example, as completed in 1816 at a cost of £1162 10s. has a 135 ft waterway.[83] Torgyle, first completed in 1809[84] and rebuilt after destruction by flood in January 1818,[85] was completed in 1826 with spans of 45, 50 and 45 ft.[86] Of the 2 span bridges, that at Greystones over the Water of Wick was noted as remarkable,[87] and the Ceanna-croc bridge was said to be 'not inconsiderable'.[88] All these, apart from the last-named, still carry traffic, as do many of the smaller structures, and numbers of those bypassed by road improvements also survive. An excellent example of an almost completely unimproved road is on the Island of Jura where there are one representative 3 span bridge and a number of typical small single span structures.

Replacement bridges. The effects of flooding on the highland bridges has already been alluded to. Before the completion of the system replacements of badly damaged or destroyed bridges were generally in similar style, though often somewhat wider in the waterway than the original design. In building substitutes for Torgyle and Drumnadrochit bridges in 1818 wood was used, though the Commissioners stated that 'the situation is such that nothing but iron bridges can be relied upon as likely to be permanent'.[88] This preoccupation with durability led the Commission to rule out wooden bridges for new construction,[89] although they flirted with the idea of using wood for Lovat Bridge.

After the new construction period had ended and the Commissioners had been given a repair remit with a limited budget, wooden replacements came into favour. The first of these was at Kirk Laggan, built in 1828 by Mr Gibb of Aberdeen. This was a 'carpentry trussed' bridge of 100 ft span, and cost roughly £1400.[90] Other medium-term replacements were over the Findhorn at Corriebrough, where Gibb built a 2 span structure for £2623[91] and the Ballater Bridge (Fig. 9) where Gibb's replacement, completed in 1834, cost £1857.[92] All these designs appear to have been Telford's. By 1830 the Commissioners were firmly committed to wooden construction, and would only pay replacement costs on that basis. When Carr Bridge over the River Dulnain required rebuilding in that year, Colonel Grant of Grant contributed an extra £500 to ensure that the replacement was in stone.[93] Beyond the Commissioners' control, the same economy prevailed. Telford's suspen-

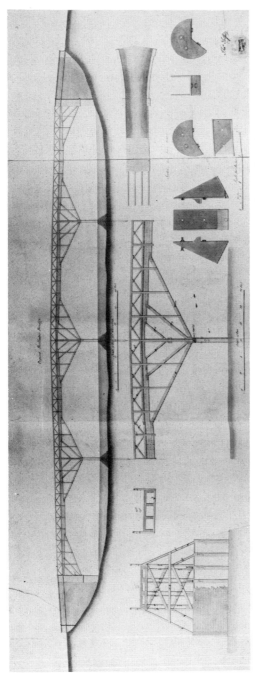

Fig. 9. The wooden bridge built to replace Ballater Bridge, showing Telford's economical use of wood (Telford Mss, Institution of Civil Engineers)

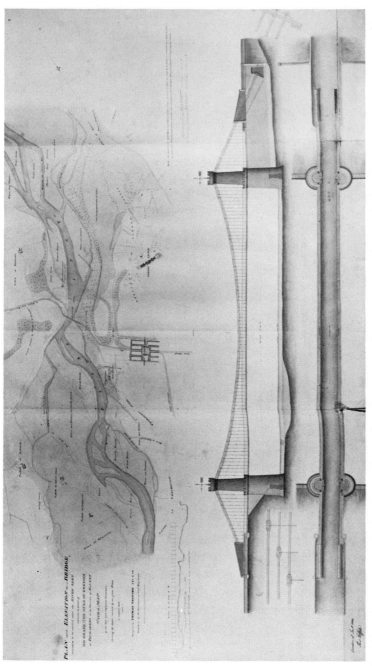

Fig. 10. The suspension bridge designed to replace the Spey Bridge at Fochabers, but not built. This was the only suspension bridge designed by Telford for Highland conditions (Telford Mss Institution of Civil Engineers)

sion bridge design (Fig. 10) to replace the washed-out spans of Fochabers Bridge[94] was rejected in favour of a laminated timber arch of about 185 ft span, designed by Archibald Simpson of Aberdeen, which lasted until the present cast-iron arch was built in 1853.[39]

Significance of Telford's highland bridges

The importance of Telford's bridges in the highlands can be assessed in a number of ways. Their contribution to the improvement of transport and communications cannot be divorced from that of the roads linking them. At the most obvious level of regular passenger and goods services their significance was striking. With the completion of the road to Thurso a 'Northern Mail Coach or Diligence' started running in July 1819. This maintained an average speed of 6 miles/h over the 159 miles, with twelve changes of horses. It carried three inside and three outside passengers as well as mail and other luggage.[95] This was the culmination of an extension of services begun in 1806, when coaches began running between Inverness and Perth. By 1828 wheeled traffic had built up substantially. Inverness had four 'manufactories for coaches' and as many as 160 coaches and gigs had been seen attending the Inverness yearly races. For goods, regular carriers were operating on all the main routes.[96] So far as communications are concerned, a letter quoted by Joseph Mitchell illustrates the improvements that had been made in services to Skye:

'Previous to the completion of the roads we had first only one, and afterwards two mails a week; and these were only carried on runners' backs. There was only one runner from Inverness to Janetown; and there being no piers or landing places, or indeed regular ferry-boats, the detention at the ferries must have been occasionally very considerable. We are now very differently situated. We have a regular communication three times a week with Dingwall, with a change of horses at different stations to the ferry of Kyleakin, and as an instance of the facility of communication, I receive a London Sunday newspaper here (Portree) every Thursday morning, a circumstance which must appear to a stranger almost incredible, and which of course is solely attributable to the roads made under the authority of the Parliamentary Commissioners'.[97]

The highland landowners, individually and as county authorities, were quick to realise the value of the new roads and bridges. In their last report original commissioners commented 'In fact the

Highland Proprietors have so largely experienced the value of their new Roads, that they are not only ready to go further in expenditure for additional roads, but have arrived at desiring roads of a quality superior to what we think prudent, in point of expense, or for other reasons desirable in the highlands.'[98] The 'superior' quality probably refers to metalling, which cost £500–600/mile, and was not standard on the Commission's roads.

By 1828 Sutherland had used statute labour money, augmented to a limited extent by landowners' contribution, to build 234 miles in extension of the Commission's roads, and similar improvement was taking place in Caithness.[99] Using these 'district roads' and the main lines, agriculture was improved not only in quality (by introducing carts, iron ploughs and harrows, and improved breeds of horses, cows, sheep and pigs) but also in extent, arable land being reclaimed from moors. Houses for all classes had been improved, and more than 40 new churches and manses had been created, largely to designs by Telford. Land values had increased markedly. The facilities provided by the roads were also of value to the ports on the east coast, through which trade with Leith and London was carried on.[100]

There is no reason to doubt Mitchell's comments. Whether the improvements quoted contributed to Telford's aim of maintaining population in the highlands[101] is more doubtful. The movement of prices for highland produce, especially black cattle, sheep and kelp, militated against the long term retention of large numbers of people on highland estates.[102] The roads which served to bring new ideas, materials and techniques into the highlands also made migration easier. In one sense this acted to reduce population, but as seasonal migration became easier this method of supplementing minimal living standards became an integral part of the highland economy.[103]

Looking at the bridges from an engineering point of view, one can quote the judgements of his biographers. Rolt commented 'Judged in terms of the sheer magnitude of the work involved and of its historical importance there can be no doubt that Telford's work in the Highlands was the greatest achievement of his career'. Rolt includes in this opinion the harbours, but not the Caledonian Canal.[104] Sir Alexander Gibb referred more specifically to the bridges:

'In his iron bridges Telford so closely studied the elimination of weight of material that they have been refined to a delicacy that has perhaps never been equalled. Such a bridge as Craigellachie Bridge surely comes near to the ideal . . . If the best of his stone bridges – Dunkeld, Bewdley and the Broomielaw – show that Telford could be the equal of the greatest in line and proportion, in his iron bridges one would be inclined to rank him first without equal among his contemporaries.'

On the lesser bridges Gibb commented that 'they are, as built, almost perfect', suggesting that the absence of ornamentation was beneficial.[105]

Certainly the whole enterprise shows Telford's great virtue as an engineer, his concern for economy, not in the short run, but in the long term. As sheer value for money, Telford's highland roads and bridges were outstanding. His innovations in the highlands – the detailed improvement of cast iron and the introduction of improved wooden bridges – were aimed at improving that value. The long term solidity of the works, which have only been substantially altered since the 1950s, is remarkable. But though one can comprehend Telford's achievements with the intellect, it is on the ground that they are most immediately impressive. Functional, but transcending the merely functional, Dunkeld and Craigellachie epitomise the grandeur of Telford's conception. Dunkeld must speak for itself, but for Craigellachie we can adopt Robert Southey's quotation about Bonar Bridge:[106]

'As I went along the road by the side of the water I could see no bridge; at last I came in sight of something like a spider's web in the air – if this be it, thought I, it will never do! But presently I came upon it, and oh, it is the finest thing that ever was made by God or man!'

Acknowledgements

The Author wishes to express his gratitude to the following people and institutions: Mr Alastair Penfold, Telford Research Fellow; the staffs of the Andersonian Library, University of Strathclyde, and of the library of the Institution of Civil Engineers, London; the Carnegie Trust for the Universities of Scotland, for grant aid towards the cost of travel in the highlands; Professor S. G. E. Lythe and Professor John Butt for help and encouragement, and last but by no means least Mrs Jean Fraser and Miss Fiona Kerr for typing the manuscript.

References

1. Hamilton H. *The industrial revolution in Scotland.* 1932, 227–228.
2. *Ibid.*, 226–7; the *Statistical Account*, edited by Sir John Sinclair and compiled in the 1790s contains several comments on the virtues of statute labour roads, for example in the parish of Old Monkland.
3. e.g. the Bridge of Dee and Brig o'Balgownie, Aberdeen; Stirling Bridge; Glasgow Bridge, demolished in the late 1840s; and the Auld Brig, Ayr
4. e.g. the Smeaton-style bridges at Coldstream, Perth, Banff, Montrose and Kenmore, and Mylne's Glasgow bridge, replaced by Telford's masterpiece in 1833.
5. Hamilton, *op. cit.*, 227.
6. *Ibid.*, 230–4; also Dott G. *Scottish colliery waggonways.* 1947; Marwick, J. D. *The River Clyde.* 1909.
7. Haldane A. R. B. *The drove roads of Scotland.* David & Charles, Newton Abbot, 1952.
8. *Ibid.*, *passim*; also Taylor W. *The military roads in Scotland.*
9. Hamilton, *op. cit.*, chaps. 2, 3; Smouth, T. C. *A history of the Scottish people, 1560–1830.* 1969, 34–7.
10. Hamilton, *op. cit.*, 60. The Society aimed to foster fisheries, trade and manufactures, as well as agricultural improvement, but also sought to preserve Gaelic cultural traditions.
11. Dunlop. *The British Fisheries Society 1786–1893.* 1978 Haldane A. R. B. *New ways through the glens.* London, Thomas Nelson, 1962, 25–27.
12. Haldane, *op. cit.*, ref. 11, 12–13.
13. Telford T. A survey and report of the coasts and Central Highlands made in the autumn of 1802. BPP 1802–3, 4, 8.
14. Bridge of Awe and Dalmally Bridge, Argyllshire were built between 1776 and 1780 with grant aid of £550 towards capital costs of £1050. See Royal Commission on the ancient and historical monuments of Scotland. Argyllshire, and *Inventory of Ancient Monuments*, 1975, Vol. 2, Lorn, 294–5. Forteviot and Kenmore bridges in Perthshire received similar assistance. See Scottish Development Department. *Lists of buildings of architectural and historic interest.*
15. Hamilton, *op. cit.*, 233, 238.
16. Buchan A. R. *The port of Peterhead, c. 1750–1914.* M Litt thesis, University of Strathclyde, 1978.
17. 9th report of Commissioners for Highland Roads and Bridges. BPP, 1821, 10, 40.
18. *Ibid.*, 49–50.
19. Haldane, *op. cit*, ref. 11. The Act was obtained on 18 July 1814; one

quarter of the cost was to be met by the Commission, the remainder by a county rate.

20. Rickman, J. *Life of Thomas Telford.* London, 1838, Appendix 8, 290–301.
21. *Ibid.*, Appendix L1, 364–9.
22. Telford, *op. cit.*, 9.
23. Rickman, *op. cit.*, Appendix L2, 369–70.
24. Quoted in Haldane, *op. cit.*, ref. 11, 35.
25. Telford, *op. cit.*, 4.
26. *Ibid.*, p. 5.
27. 4th report of Commissioners. BPP, 1809, 4, 8.
28. *Ibid.*, 10.
29. As at Craigellachie; HLRO, 26 July 1813.
30. 6th report of Commissioners. BPP, 1812–13, 5, 10–11.
31. *Ibid.*, 10.
32. *Ibid.*, 24.
33. 7th report of Commissioners. BPP, 1814–15, 3, 445.
34. 16th report of Repair Commissioner. BPP, 1830, 15, 87.
35. Telford, *op. cit.*, 4.
36. *Ibid.*, 5.
37. 4th report of Commissioners. BPP, 1809, 4, 19; 8th report of Commissioners. 1817, 9, 28.
38. Telford, *op. cit.*, 6; 3rd report of Commissioners. BPP, 1807, 3, 258.
39. Booth L. G. Laminated timber arch railway bridges in England and Scotland: written communication by J. G. James *Trans. Newcomen Soc.*, 1971–2, 44, 18.
40. Hume J. R. Cast iron in bridge building in Scotland. *Industr. Archaeol. Rev.*
41. Telford, *op. cit.*, 7.
42. 4th report of Commissioners. BPP. 1809, 4, 19.
43. 3rd report of Commissioners. BPP, 1807, 3, 258.
44. 4th report of Commissioners. BPP, 1809, 4, 20.
45. 6th report of Commissioners. BPP, 1812–13, 5, 26.
46. 7th report of Commissioners. BPP, 1814–15, 3, 445.
47. Telford, *op. cit.*, 11.
48. Southey R. *Journal of a tour in Scotland, 1819.* 1929, 129. also 5th report of Commissioners. BPP, 1810–11, 4, 438.
49. 4th report of Commissioners. BPP, 1809, 4, 15.
50. 5th report of Commissioners. BPP, 1810–11, 4, 412.
51. Telford Atlas. (See Gibb, Sir A. *The story of Telford.* London, Alexander Machose, 1935, facing p. 136).
52. 6th report of Commissioners. BPP, 1812–13, 5, 26 (I have not found

any evidence to support Rolt's statement that the bridge was designed with two 150 ft spans).

53. *Ibid.*, 27.
54. *Ibid.*, 28.
55. *Ibid.*, Appendix C.
56. 13th report of Repair Commissioners. BPP, 1826–7, 7, 107.
57. Its replacement was built in 1892 by Crouch and Hogg, whose second bridge on this site was completed in 1974; in elegance it compares well with Telford's design.
58. 6th report of Commissioners. BPP, 1812–13, 5, 19.
59. 8th report of Commissioners, 1817, 9, 24.
60. 20th report of Repair Commissioners. BPP, 1834, 40, 165.
61. 7th report of Commissioners. BPP, 1814–15, 3, 442.
62. 5th report of Commissioners. BPP, 1810–11, 4, 410.
63. *Ibid.*, 412.
64. 2nd report of Commissioners. BPP, 1807, 3, 257.
66. 4th report of Commissioners. BPP, 1809, 4, 19.
67. 3rd report of Commissioners. 1807, 3, 257–8.
68. 5th report of Commissioners. BPP, 1810–11, 4, 411.
69. Haldane, *op. cit.*, ref. 11, 130.
70. 5th report of commissioners. BPP, 1810–11, 4, 411.
71. 6th report of Commissioners. BPP, 1812–13, 5, 24.
72. 7th report of Commissioners. BPP, 1814–15, 3, 444.
73. 5th report of Commissioners. BPP, 1810–11, 4, 411; 6th report. BPP, 1812–13, 5, 24.
74. 6th report of Commissioners, BPP, 1812–13, 5, 12.
75. 7th report of Commissioners. BPP, 1814–15, 3, 435.
76. 16th report of Repair Commissioners. BPP, 1830, 15, 87.
77. 5th report of Commissioners. BPP, 1810–11, 4, 411.
78. 6th report of Commissioners. BPP, 1812–13, 5, 25.
79. 7th report of Commissioners. BPP, 1814–15, 3, 445.
80. 16th report of Repair Commissioners. BPP, 1830, 15, 87.
81. Rickman, *op. cit.*, 169–70.
82. 1st report of Commissioners. 1803–4, 5, Appendix K.
83. 8th report of Commissioners. BPP, 1817, 9, 21.
84. 5th report of Commissioners. BPP, 1810–11, 4, 403.
85. 9th report of Commissioners. BPP, 1821, 10, 61.
86. 12th report of Repair Commissioners. BPP, 1826, 11, 59.
87. 9th report of Commissioners. BPP, 1821, 10, 72.
88. *Ibid.*, 61.
89. 3rd report of Commissioners. BPP, 1807, 3, 257; 4th report. BPP, 1809, 4, 10.

90. 15th report of Repair Commissioners, BPP, 1829, 5, 135.
91. 19th report of Repair Commissioners. BPP, 1833, 17, 405.
92. 20th report of Repair Commissioners. BPP, 1834, 10, 87; see also Telford drawing, Telford Mss, Institution of Civil Engineers.
93. 17th report of Repair Commissioners. BPP, 1830–1, 4, 380.
94. Telford drawing. Telford Mss, ICE Library.
95. 9th report of Commissioners. BPP, 1821, 73.
96. Rickman, *op. cit.*, Appendix L11. Mitchell, J. *Improved state of the Highlands of Scotland . . . with Notices of the results.* 1828, *passim.*
97. *Ibid.*, 462.
98. 9th report of the Commissioners. BPP, 1821, 10, 47.
99. Rickman, *op. cit.*, Appendix S2, 462–3; *New statistical account. Caithness, passim.*
100. Rickman, *op. cit.*, Appendix 52, passim.
101. Telford, *op. cit.*, quoted in Rickman, *op. cit.*, 301.
102. See, for example, Gray, M. *The highland economy.* 1957; and, for an extreme view, Prebble, J. *The highland clearances.*
103. T. M. Devine.
104. Rolt, *op. cit.*, 83.
105. Gibb, *op. cit.*, 263.
106. Southey, *op. cit.*, quoted by Rolt, *op. cit.*, 88.